ENTOMOLOGICAL

INFORMATION

STORAGE

AND

RETRIEVAL

ENTOMOLOGICAL INFORMATION

STORAGE AND RETRIEVAL

Ross H. Arnett, Jr.

Professor of Entomology
Purdue University
Lafayette, Indiana

The Bio-Rand Foundation, Inc.

1330 Dillon Heights Avenue
Baltimore, Maryland 21228

"The complex nature of living things necessarily gives rise to a complex methodology for studying them and thus generating a host of complex problems that make it difficult to retrieve information about them. The recording of the information a scientist obtains as he studies a given problem probably does not present a great difficulty, but the investigator who tries to uncover for himself what someone else has already discovered about a living thing, a methodology, or a principle often finds his task virtually insurmountable."

—Richard H. Foote, *Dallas, 1968*

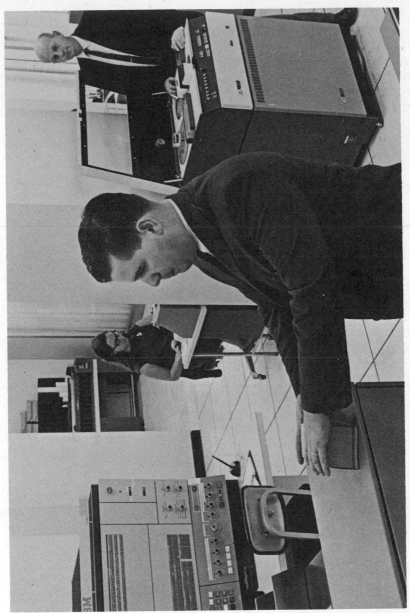

Frontispiece. Information processing using electronic data-processing equipment at BIOSIS. (Courtesy Biological Abstracts, Philadelphia, Pa.)

PREFACE

Objectives:

This guide is designed for the use of all entomologists to aid them in their search for entomological information. It is concerned primarily with:

The entomological literature and its efficient use

Means for keeping up to date in the special branches of entomology

The literature and information needed to prepare research papers and have them published

The use of our system of binominal nomenclature and an introduction to the International Code of Zoological Nomenclature as they relate to information storage and retrieval

The theory of information storage and retrieval systems

Methods of improving entomological communication including reference to all recommendations of the Committee on Scientific and Technical Communication (SATCOM Report, 1969).

Prerequisites:

Those undertaking a study of entomological information retrieval should know how to use the library card catalog and have a general knowledge of their own available libraries. It is assumed also that they have had some experience with some kinds of entomological literature. Beyond this, the guide is self-explanatory.

Use of the guide:

This book is intended to be little more than an introduction to a complicated subject. However, enough information is included to enable students or professional entomologists to work with confidence with the entomological literature and to give them some control over the information log jam. After diligent study one can learn how to keep up to date with the entomological subjects of his special interest and by the application of the methods described herein, to save time in his literature search.

The annotated list of basic entomology reference books has been carefully selected to acquaint the user with those works which will lead one deeper into the subject. In addition to the works referred to in the text, this bibliography contains additional useful references. Therefore the user should consult the bibliography for further information on the subject matter of each chapter.

Ten study exercises, each with a number of parts, are included as practice assignments. After completion of each of these, the review checklist will help to determine whether the points covered have been learned.

Special emphasis has been made to provide the user with a modern glossary of terms to help him learn the new information retrieval jargon. All terms used for the first time in the text are placed in italics and are defined in the glossary.

While the book was being written, the SATCOM Report appeared. Each of the many recommendations made by the Committee on Scientific and Technical Communication of the National Academy of Science and the National Academy of Engineering has been carefully considered and referred to in this book. The user may wish to consult that work to understand its importance as an appraisal of the current problem of information storage and retrieval. Having done so, he will no doubt agree that the literature of science has greatly increased in complexity at least in certain fields, and that there is need for new methods of information handling. Although the crisis may not be as acute in entomology as in other sciences, new methods now being used in other fields will affect the entomological literature as well.

Optional investigations:

Many users may find it necessary to make a further study of the various topics discussed in this text. After many of the basic assignments is a suggested project, or "optional investigation" which is designed to help one attain competence in independent handling of entomological information.

Materials needed to complete assignments
suggested in this text:

Although the book may be used by many outside of the classroom, those who may wish to complete the assignments for more formal classroom use will find the following items necessary.

A supply of 3 x 5 file cards and tab index separators
Cardboard or metal 3 x 5 card storage file large enough to hold
  1,000 cards
A supply of standard IBM-type punch cards
A copy of the following (see bibliography for complete reference):
  Style Manual for Biological Journals
  Guide to the Preparation of Abstracts (BIOSIS)
  Guide to the Indexes . . . (BIOSIS)

In order to complete the assignments utilizing automatic data processing and computer programming access to such equipment is necesary.

Acknowledgments:

During the course of writing this guide the author became a member of the Special Committee on Information Retrieval of the Entomological Society of America. The work with this Committee was a great aid to the author in crystalizing ideas and as a source of much new information. I am particularly grateful to several people for their time in reading and commenting on the text. Drs. Ronald L. Giese and Virginia Ferris of the Department of Entomology, Purdue University, and Dr. Rosalie A. Dunn, Georgetown University read the entire book and offered many valuable suggestions which brought about revisions in the text. In addition, Dr. Giese rewrote the computer program discussed herein and provided me with this portion of the text. Dr. Richard E.

Blackwelder of Southern Illinois University, Carbondale, with his usual keen perception, pointed out several ways to make the text more lucid, for which I am grateful. Drs. Charles and Lois O'Brien, Texas Tech University, Lubbock, discussed many points with me in the early stages of writing. This was a great help and I appreciate their friendly interest.

This book was written because I felt that there was a need for a modern teaching manual on this subject. But I would never have been bold enough to attempt this project if it hadn't been for the continued encouragement of two colleagues, Drs. Richard H. Foote, United States Department of Agriculture, Beltsville, and H. E. Kennedy, Bioscience Information Service, Philadelphia. Both men took time out to review the manuscript in various stages of development. Their suggestions and guidance gave me the courage to offer the book for publication. Since neither Dr. Foote nor Dr. Kennedy have read the final manuscript entirely and critically evaluated the book, no reader should attribute any of its shortcomings to either of these men or to any of the other reviewers.

I am grateful also to Dr. N. M. Downie for his interest and encouragement and to Mr. David Held for his aid with the illustrations. Finally, the keen interest shown by my students in my class at Purdue University as they used the early xeroxed drafts of the book has been most encouraging and helpful in completing the project.

So, in spite of many interruptions, the book has been completed. If any reader has read this far, I ask that he now turn to the end of the book and read the *Postface*, since it is obvious that he is entertained by the personal views and comments of authors.

R.H.A.
Lafayette, Indiana, January 1970

CONTENTS

LIST OF ILLUSTRATIONS

CHAPTER 1

INTRODUCTION—THE INFORMATION PROBLEM

Space age science has affected all branches of science by leading the way toward mechanized research. The astronomers of yesterday patiently mapped the surface of the moon and the planets by means of a telescope. Today they send a space craft to do their work, a vehicle made possible by the use of a new research tool, the *computer.** Even though the basic work of the scientists of the past led the way, their work was made pitifully obsolete on July 20, 1969. Long hours of dreary observation and manual recording of *data* has provided us with our basic *information* resources. This slow process of scientific re-search is now aided by rapid, highly accurate, automatic equipment. As a result of the speed at which he can now make his calculations the scientist is freed to spend more time in thinking, and less in procedural matters.

At the same time our insatiable thirst for more knowledge results in the gathering and recording of great amounts of complex data. We have not only an accumulation of approximately 5,000 years of written

* See glossary for definitions of all technical terms placed in italics the first time used in the text.

1

records, but the rate of gathering data in some areas of science increases logrithmically. Scientists believe that research is not complete until all of the data are made available in hard form, i.e., *publications,* usually by *printing.*

We find now that we have gathered vast amounts of data, organized these into information packages called *documents* most of which are stored in the form of publications or other record forms, and have made little provision for their retrieval. In fact, at the present time, we are faced with the shocking realization that retrieval may be even more time consuming than the original data gathering procedure. This is an information crisis—one more problem of our life in a crowded world.

INFORMATION SOURCES

The entomologist, as any scientist, depends upon observations as the ultimate source for his information. From direct observations or indirect records made with the aid of instruments, he gathers his data and produces information about the organization of the insects or the phenomenon he is observing.

INFORMATION SOURCES

 Observation and experimentation
 Specimens and samples
 Literature and related stored records

Information in printed form, which is produced from observations and distributed to libraries and individuals, is referred to as the *litera-ture.* Not all available information is stored as literature. Photographs, movies, slides, and charts, some of which may be available in duplicated copies and some only as originals, are also information sources (see chapter 3). In addition, data processing equipment using punch cards, tapes, iron cores, and other means, store data and provide additional information sources. Because the term literature has restricted meaning, the term record is now used to refer to any durable packet of information used in the communication of facts. The records suitable for storage and retrieval are referred to as *source documents.* These are stored as file cards, typescript, punch cards, electronic tape, iron core, and printed records.

KINDS OF DATA USED IN ENTOMOLOGY

Scientific progress, practically speaking, is the result of two things:

1) The organization of the available information.
2) The active search for supplementary data to complete the information necessary to demonstrate a fact.

It is not by chance that many of the great discoveries of the past have been made by several persons almost simultaneously. Once a certain amount of information becomes available it is natural that the educated minds of several scientists working independently will piece together the separate facts. They test their ideas, often in different ways, until they have gathered enough facts to support their thesis. With this information available they write a report of their discoveries. As we shall see later, it is the association of the facts from each of the many sources as efficiently as possible that permits still further discoveries in the future. If we can make machinery do the work, more time is available to the entomologist to do more research—the goal of information management.

Observation data are records of information gathered by human senses generally unaided or through the use of optical and measuring instruments. Experimental data are observation data gathered from controlled or compared situations as planned and executed by the scientist. There is no real distinction between these two data sources, although some entomologists are known as experimenters, and others as observers (see Arnett, 1966). Light microscopes and cameras are the usual aids used for the gathering of these data. For the taxonomic entomologist information about the shape, size, structure, and color of insects, their habitats, and plant and animal associates constitutes the recorded data. The economic entomologist uses data concerning the size, fluctuation, parasites, and physiological reactions of populations. They compare data on populations, especially as they react to various physical, chemical, and biological factors as they occur both under natural and under experimental conditions. Still other branches of the science use other types of data. Weights, lengths, and proportions add to the information, but sometimes more complex measurements are necessary when making these studies. Oscilloscopes and other electronic instruments record all such data. Digital computers are able to process this type of information once it is converted into a form for computer storage.

NEED FOR NEW METHODS FOR HANDLING INFORMATION

Once it was possible for a naturalist to scan the titles listed on the covers of the issues of the few available publications and feel that he was reasonably current in his field of interest. Even if he missed a publication here and there, it did not cause much worry, for the paper was sure to be brought to his attention by a colleague. To a considerable extent this practice is still followed, and this is one of the reasons for the continued popularity of regional and national meetings. But because of the explosive generation of data in the past 100 years, and the resulting documents, one can no longer make an information search without a carefully planned system. Browsing as a system of *current awareness* is little more than "hit-or-miss." Unless one is able to conduct a thorough information search, many man-hours of time will be wasted in duplicated effort. Many libraries are concerned over the lack of space in which to store masses of seldom used archival material duplicated many hundreds of times and stored the world over to be locally available when and if they are needed. At the present rate, scientific libraries double every 15 years (more rapidly than the population explosion!), and, since 1951 as much scientific data have been published as existed previously. At the same time, retrieval of information from a library remains a slow process at best. Much needs to be done and is being done to improve library service in the modern world (SATCOM recommendations C5 and C6, SATCOM Report, 1969).*

WHAT CAN BE DONE

The efficient gathering of more knowledge without repeating what is already known depends upon finding out what we now have. To do this, systems of organization of data are required. These vary from the simple indexing systems of books, bibliographic references, abstracts, and file card indexes, to modern methods of *electronic data processing (EDP)*. Using punch cards, magnetic tape, and similar materials makes possible greater speed in information retrieval. We need to

*See Preface and Bibliography.

increase the efficiency of all of the current systems of information storage and retrieval to get back this information.

THE ORGANIZATION OF THIS BOOK

The chapters that follow deal with the current sources of entomological information and describe means of improving upon their use. This book is arranged in three parts:

1) Theory of information storage and retrieval (chapter 2) followed by three chapters on information storage.
2) Preparation of documents for retrieval and two chapters on aids to information retrieval.

These first two parts are devoted almost entirely to original information sources.

3) The final three chapters discuss briefly the various secondary information sources.

The user of this book should note that each topic is considered only in sufficient depth to enable him to continue on his own into the world of stored information. With these principles in mind he should find no difficulty in becoming well acquainted with the data available in his special branch of the study of entomology.

The three appendixes at the end of the volume provide lists of some useful information unavailable elsewhere. Appendix I may serve as a guide for the assembling of a personal library on entomology, and the basis for a school library on the subject. Appendix II gives the entomobibliophile the names of firms to write to for catalogs and a place to order more volumes to build the entomology library. Appendix III lists the source of materials needed to organize the insect specimens as information files (see text). Finally, Appendix IV indicates the best sources for the third kind of available information, that stored in libraries.

REVIEW CHECKLIST

1. Define the following terms as used in this chapter (see glossary):
   Computer; Current awareness; Document; Information; Literature; Printing; Publication; Record; Source document

2. Libraries, under present conditions, are faced with two problems; what are they?
3. What are the information sources that must be used in entomology?
4. How does research get duplicated, i.e., the same work done by two or more scientists at two or more locations? Is this always disadvantagous?
5. State the nature of the information problem in your own words.

CHAPTER 2

INFORMATION STORAGE AND RETRIEVAL
SYSTEMS THEORY

The problem of handling information and the newness of our concern is reflected in the titles of discussions at the Sixth Annual National Information Retrieval Colloquium in 1969: privacy and information technology; describing documents; information dissemination systems; library automation; the data conversion muddle; models and criteria for design of retrieval systems, and so on.

The two terms, data and information, are frequently used as if they were synonyms. However, by considering their separate meaning, the subject matter of this chapter is clarified. Data pertains to facts or statistics, either historical or derived from calculations or observations. These data are gathered and stored in various ways. This storage of data is known as a record. The data in these records may be used in a computer and be changed as a result of this processing so that when retrieved from the computer the new record produced is different from the original. For example, measurements, the data taken from specimens, may be processed to find the standard deviation and coefficient of variation of a population. The record that results differs from the original. The process used to produce the new record is termed a *data retrieval system (DRS)* and makes use of *automatic data processing (ADP)* or *electronic data processing (EDP)* equipment.

Information refers to the communication of data, usually by means of a document available in the form of a publication or record. Information differs from data as used in the example in the preceding paragraph in that it is already processed as an organized set of data. The processing includes assemblage into a form that carries a reference, or as it is sometimes called, an address. The information package has a title in addition to the reference, and, recently, additional descriptions of the contents such as an *abstract* and *descriptors* or *key words.* The purpose of an *information retrieval system (IRS)* is to locate records, particularly documents, through the use of descriptors to find the reference or address of the document. To do this, there must be an *information bank* containing these descriptors and references. For example, a document may describe a new species. When we process such a document, we wish to pass on and use unchanged the data contained in the document. Thus the information stored and retrieved is unchanged by the computer or by any of the other data processing equipment used. The information bank is a part of an *information center* that builds and·maintains the information bank and the information system (IRS).

Do not suppose that the only thing necessary to solve the problems of information storage and retrieval is to process available documents or records for electronic data processing (EDP). No system is yet available that will store such a vast amount of data. Nor is there any implication that all publications will or should disappear. The matter of funds, user needs, and convenience, as well as the time needed to build a system are limiting factors. These form a three-way tension that determines the nature of any IRS. The availability of funds is directly related to the frequency of use of the system and the efficiency of the operation. Information resulting from data properly organized and tested is best presented in the old fashioned desk top "information center"—books. Before an IRS can be of use to us, many hours of professional thought and work are necessary. Information banks are still tedious to build, and like most publications, they go out-of-date and need constant attention. Potential users of IRS's resist change. The designers of an IRS must clearly demonstrate the time saving advantage of the system.

INFORMATION AND DATA CENTERS

Provide depositories for documents used in Selective Dissemination of Information (SDI) (SATCOM recommendation E9)

Maintain data and information banks on tape or in disc packs, and participate in a network of information centers (SATCOM recommendations B5, part 3, B14, E2, and E3)

Coordinate index and code terms through a master thesaurus

Produce specialized data reference packages with provision for frequent up-dating (SATCOM recommendations B1, B5, part 2)

Establish library network with telecopiers (SATCOM recommendation E1)

Provide technical report clearinghouses

Coordinate existing abstracting services and make up any deficiencies (SATCOM recommendations B10, and B11)

Coordinate meetings, advance notice of contents, coordination of meeting plans, especially for symposia and contributed papers (SATCOM recommendations B6 and C16)

Coordinate educational needs (SATCOM recommendation B5, part 4)

Cooperate with the proposed Joint Commission of Scientific and Technical Communication, and make provisions for keeping abreast of developments in scientific and technical communication (SATCOM recommendations A1, A11, and B9)

Exchange information with the government, other scientific organizations, including foreign organizations and private groups (SATCOM recommendations A2, A3, A5, A6, and A7)

Secure grant and contract support for the development of information and data centers (SATCOM recommendations A4, B2, B7, B8, and E10)

Develop methods of protecting individuals or corporate ownership of document and record distribution packages to preserve broad and rapid accessibility of information, maintain incentives to distribute this information and protect the investment of time and materials (SATCOM recommendation A10)

THEORETICAL CAPACITY OF A SYSTEM

The use of electronic data processing (EDP) equipment to speed up information retrieval is a relatively recent development in the field of information theory, which is, in turn, an extension of probability theory. The use of computers and communication networks may seem, because of the great popular interest in the subject, to provide for unlimited storage and retrieval of information and data. There is a distinct mathematical limitation to the information storage possibilities. The time is still distant when all information will be stored for instant retrieval (Lipetz, 1966).

Information theory is formalized by quantitative units representing the information content. Because data are stored as *binary digits* (shortened to *bits*), the amount of information in a message is expressed in terms of the probability of a sequence of binary choices or bits. This may be expressed in mathematical formulae and partially explains the function and operation of the computer at high speed.

The capacity of present equipment, in spite of its mammoth storage possibilities, is far less than the most simple protein molecules. The DNA molecule stores a complete and complex program for the growth and development of a cell which far surpasses any present day storage bank of information. For example, it is claimed that a single, relatively small bacterial cell contains about 10^{12} bits of information. Compared with a set of the *Encyclopedia Britannica*, each page of which has about 10^6 bits, each volume of which has 10^9 bits (per 1,000 pages), the bacterial cell's 10^{12} bits contains as much information as 1,000 volumes of 1,000 pages each of this work. Even as we work to change present systems to EDP, we foresee further difficulties to come. Perhaps the solution lies in emulating the DNA molecule in the EDP system.

INFORMATION CYCLE

All kinds of information must first be gathered, then processed, and stored for future retrieval. This information cycling began with the first records left by early man, and continues at an ever increasing rate. The cycle of information processing shown here (figure 1) is one method of data organization. The boxes in the chart represent various phases of research and study, while the arrows indicate the direction of the flow of the information as it is processed, stored, and used. The

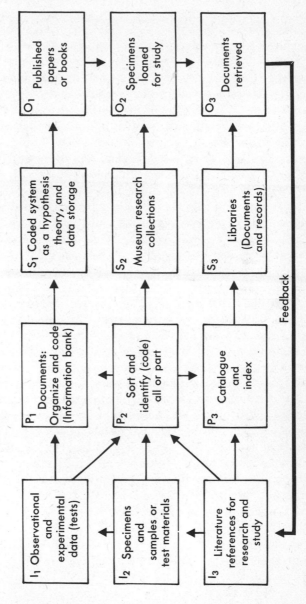

Fig. 1. The Information Cycle showing the stages and pathways of information and data processing.

simplest statement that can be made to describe this cycle is: gather, evaluate, code, store, and retrieve. Data are stored in various stages of processing according to the type of research activity involved. For example, the information being processed may involve the distribution data for a single species, or the response of a test insect to a certain chemical. Or the system may be used to organize and retrieve more complex data for the production of a monograph. Notice the similarity of this to the classical stages of the so-called Scientific Method. Data or information are gathered from all information sources. The organization of the data or information leads to the formation of a hypothesis. This is reflected in the coding, e.g., the organization leads to topics and subtopics; the identification leads to naming, and the literature after indexing, to the known information. The repetition of these first two steps is the testing of the hypothesis. Finally, when enough information is associated, organized, and stored, one may formulate a theory. When this is made available through retrieval in some form of a publication, sorted specimens, or documents, the cycle may be repeated. These phases of the information cycle are followed each time new facts are discovered.

A detailed examination of figure 1 shows, in somewhat simplified form, all of the aspects of research and of data processing treated as a part of research. It should be understood that data processing is used by many others in our modern world. It is not confined to research. The elementary discussion in this book is, however, restricted to the use of these processes for academic study and research.

All source materials are grouped into three categories. Data derived from observation and experimentation are the original or primary source of all information (source document no. I_1). These are the records in notebooks, on cards, or as charts, photographs, and tapes that are to be organized. In certain kinds of research, information is stored as raw data in the form of specimens and their labels, or as samples of material (source document no. I_2). Through the use of preserved specimens in near original condition records are available so that additional data may be gathered from them at any time. This is noted on the diagram by the arrow which connects with source document I_1. Finally information is gathered by a study of the literature, indicated by source document I_3. It should be noted that retrieved information may be fed back into the system and it becomes a source of information for a new cycle.

After the source materials are gathered, the processing begins. Each type of material is coded according to its nature, following a carefully designed code description system (P_1, P_2 and P_3). Words used as a title describe documents prepared from the information in I_1, as for example, the genetics, evolution, development, or taxonomy of a group, and many others. These documents may be further coded by the addition of descriptors. Specimens and samples (I_2), must be identified (P_2) either as chemicals, using chemical names, or organisms, using names available according to our system of binominal nomenclature. All available literature (I_3) is used to make these identifications. Identifications, therefore, are a form of code names, or *code terms*. These, in turn, are added to the documents (arrow to P_1). Finally, the literature (I_3), itself is catalogued and indexed as a literature document (P_3), to form a card file or a bibliography of these source-documents.

The source documents and records, now coded, must be processed for storage. Storage procedures vary according to the nature of the records and the method to be followed for the eventual retrieval. Therefore, storage processing is concerned mainly with the organization of the coded source materials so that they may be retrieved. Data contained in documents is organized as hypotheses and/or theories. The organized data (P_1) used to arrive at these hypotheses or theories now are ready for storage. Therefore, S_1 is a document ready for publication by one or more of the several methods possible.

Prepared specimens (P_2) are stored as collections arranged according to the identification code (S_2), and according to the classification followed. This classification may be one proposed as S_1. Some kinds of research using samples do not require the preservation of specimens so S_2 samples are discarded.

Library collections (S_3) are arranged according to the coding system adopted by the operator of the library, i.e., the library classification system arrangement.

Retrieval of each of the information source materials is now possible. If S_1 documents are published (O_1) they are retrieved through the cataloguing system (P_3) used by libraries. Their contents have been coded by means of an index as an aid to retrieval and each has been given an address in the form of a bibliographic reference. These, then, become a part of S_3 and are retrieved as O_3. Specimens and samples (O_2) needed for further study or reference are retrieved by looking for information under the names of the organisms or chemicals. These documents, once retrieved by any of the several means available, are used as an aid for further information processing and the cycle is repeated.

ASSIGNMENT 1

1.1 After studying the text, relate the theory presented to any IRS. Make a list of at least 3 EDP systems used in your everyday activities and describe the pathway of each activity through the information cycle (figure 1); use only the letters and subscripts needed to do this. Tell what the process is at each stage.

1.2 Visit a library, a research museum, and a research laboratory. Study the organization of each and locate the applicable stages and pathways of the activities of these organizations following the cycle shown in figure 1. Describe very briefly these stages by giving a specific example of each as observed during your visit.

PRINCIPLES OF SYSTEM DESIGN

Research and development (R. and D.) in this space age world requires teamwork; there is little room for a tempermental entomologist to hide away in seclusion if he expects to keep up with current progress. Teams of specialists are able to coordinate their plans through the use of a logical procedure termed a *system design*. This outlines the major steps and describes each in detail so that all concerned may know stages needed and their value. They are able by this means to grasp the whole while dealing with the particular. The idea of system design is to break down a big problem into smaller, easier-to-solve problems. The system is, therefore, a cycle of steps repeated as often as necessary to complete the job. *Flowcharts* are used to help design efficient systems during a system analysis. A flowchart starts with the *input* information or materials. Step by step stages in the processing of the information or material is pictured throughout the system. Then the final *output* of processed information or materials is shown. The hardware configuration needed for a particular job usually becomes obvious when a flowchart is used in a system analysis.

The first phase in planning a project is to define objectives. This should be done as concisely as possible without explanations or procedure included as a part of the objective. For example, an objective might be:

To acquire a collection of adult insects occurring in Tippecanoe

County, Indiana.

It is improper to state an objective as follows:

To collect by black-light and similar standard means representatives of the insects occurring in Tippecanoe County, Indiana, and to mount, label, and arrange these as a local collection.

The details and procedure mentioned in this second statement only obscures the real objective, that of acquiring a collection. Several related objectives may be necessary to any given project. These are stated in the same concise manner as the first example above.

The second step is to outline each of the possible ways to reach these objectives. Several alternative systems may, and usually should, be planned, including the steps in use if a system is currently in operation either at the institution or elsewhere.

Careful comparative evaluation of each of the proposed systems is then necessary. This evaluation should include both costs and effectiveness or efficiency of the systems to reach the objective. The efficiency can be determined only in terms of time in relation to the cost (see p. 38).

Next begins a critique of both the objectives and the assumptions made in stating the objectives. In other words, is the project worth it? Will the service justify the costs? This analysis may then lead the investigator to change certain objectives and establish new goals. If such is the case, then the modified system will need the same scrutiny and the cycle is repeated.

Once these steps are followed for each of the phases of the system design, the parts are brought together and arranged harmoniously. To do this, the time sequences of each of the steps must fit, and the work load and volume of output passing from one stage to the next must balance. To help coordinate activities, a *PERT* chart (Figure 2) is made. On this chart the time allotted for each phase and the deadline for the completion of each activity is plotted. For instance if an information retrieval system requires that the user sort through many thousands of cards at random to retrieve, with a time delay of many minutes, which makes a backlog at that point in the flow through the system, redesign is necessary. The PERT chart soon shows the phases that are out of balance and adjustments in the system design may be made. The purpose of this kind of system analysis is, obviously, to aid in the careful planning of a project. Once the analysis has been com-

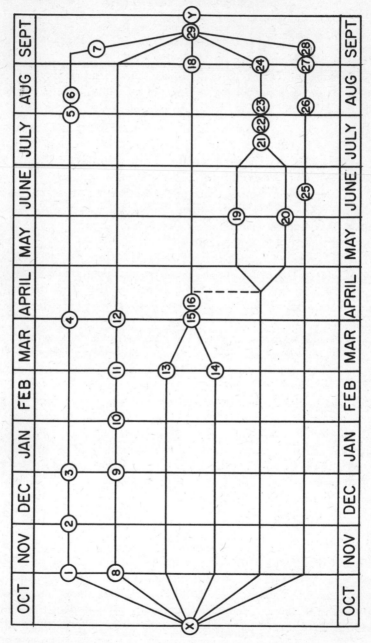

Fig. 2. A PERT chart showing the steps from input to output with monthly coördination.

pleted, the proposal is written. Each of the numbers in Figure 2 represents a stage or process, all of which must be coordinated when writing the proposal. The use of flowcharts and PERT charts to coordinate each phase of the system forces the designer to think through each stage.

SYSTEM DESIGN

    Define objectives
    Possible alternatives to reach objectives
    Evaluation of proposed system
    Critique of objectives
    Modify system
    Assemble parts and coordinate by means of a PERT chart
    Prepare proposal

ASSIGNMENT 1 (Cont.)

1.3 Plan a method to achieve one of the following objectives by using the steps of system design discussed previously. Write out your analysis and illustrate the system with a simple flowchart and a PERT chart. Objectives:

1.31 To acquire a collection of adult insects occuring in Tippecanoe County, Indiana.

1.32 To purchase a new automobile.

1.33 To organize and produce a notebook storing information on [a subject of your choice].

OPTIONAL INVESTIGATION

Apply the principles of system analysis to the design and proposal of a simple research project.

DESIGN AND OPERATION OF AN IRS

Information storage and retrieval systems are designed using the principles of information theory and system design. Each IRS must be designed for a particular project using the principles discussed earlier in this chapter. Several steps may be followed in IRS design, but each must be given long thought, much discussion, and be adapted to the objectives promulgated. Figure 3 diagrams the various stages necessary for the design and operations of an IRS

DESIGN OF AN IRS

Survey of the information requirements of potential users
Design of a prototype
    File characteristics
    Percentage of retrieval
    Coding procedure
    Retrieval procedure
Test of prototype
    Process search requests
    Quality control
Revise system
Operate
Maintain quality control

Survey of the information requirement in entomology.—Entomological information is both *discipline oriented* and *mission oriented*. Teachers and the so-called "pure" scientists (those not directly concerned with development) are usually involved in a range of subject matter that is several phases of a single discipline. For example, to study pollen feeding beetles, one is concerned not only with the structure and habits of the beetles involved, but with flowers, pollen morphology, and plant taxonomy. So a discipline oriented information bank must store a wide but selected range of topics. Mission oriented information banks will serve somewhat more practical needs, but the range of topics will be just as broad. For example, an information bank on the use of DDT and its effects would be much larger than many discipline oriented stores.

A review of the type and scope of existing information sources (see next chapter, Stored Information) must be made. User needs and the categories of user interest must be understood for efficient processing of documents as well as *search requests*. The survey should include information on the economics of the operation.

The way to determine the exact details of user interests, needs, and the economics of an IRS is beyond the scope of this present treatment of the subject. The available literature on this subject is growing each day. Although a systems analyst is required for the final design of an IRS center, often a user interest, use potential, and resources survey can be conducted by sending questionnaires to the membership of a large society. This applies only if a discipline oriented system is contemplated. Mission oriented systems are generally for the use of a specific project and its personnel. Questionnaires must be carefully designed for ease in interpretation and evaluation of the results by the analyst. Too many amateur questionnaires already have made many otherwise cooperative individuals wary of these forms. Unless properly designed, much of the information is either lost or useless even when the forms are completed.

Design of a prototype system.—The first step in the establishment of the IRS is the design of the information *search file*. This must be made compatible with 1) optimum output characteristics; 2) properties of the information bank, and 3) the processing procedure. The entomological information bank is discussed in the chapters on stored information and original documents in this book. Some of the output characteristics and processing procedures, except for *information coding*, are considered briefly below.

In forming the policy of the search file characteristics, one must decide upon the level of exhaustivity to employ in indexing and coding. In some fields, as in taxonomic entomology, this is not so difficult. The International Code of Zoological Nomenclature (see chapter on information coding) provides rules for deciding what publications containing new descriptions must be indexed and stored. Other disciplines may be able to limit their search file by starting at a mutually acceptable date. Still others may limit their input to a standard list of *core journals* and perhaps a relatively few additional peripheral publications. In entomology, core journals are publications with 85 to 90% of their articles on entomology. Many other source materials are available (see following chapters on abstracts, *synthesized information*, societies, institutions, and personnel).

The theoretically perfect IRS would have all information sources processed and stored in the information files so that 100% retrieval might be achieved. This is possible only in bookkeeping and banking files where complete control is maintained over the information source. No current system is available to adequately screen all sources of entomological information. This could be done only if the system had control over all sources of retrieval. If this is accepted as a working premise, the analyst is able to evaluate the various objectives of the proposed system and design an efficient and useful system. Even though he doesn't get 100% retrieval, his goal will be reached.

Processing in the prototype IRS.—Coding of information content is the most critical stage of an IRS. Usually a basic *thesaurus* is established. The information documents are analyzed for subject content and coded. This involves not only an index language, but a conceptual analysis. The latter cannot be done by technicians alone, but requires the aid of specialists including the authors themselves. (Details of coding are discussed in the chapter on Information Coding.) The same coding is required of the search requests as well, and the success of the system depends upon the matching of the document profile with the request profiles (this is discussed in detail in the chapter on Search Resources).

Output products.—The possibilities for information output (retrieval) are limited only by the designer's imagination and the efficiency of the input. Four main categories of output are generally considered in any system. These are: 1) current awareness; 2) *retrospective search*; 3) *references* to the location of source materials, and 4) the *taxonomic data file*. Until very recently current awareness needs were met by the prompt publication of abstracts. This no longer suffices. Even more rapid communication centers are being designed and may soon be in operation. For example, various governmental agencies are processing progress reports so that instant retrieval by means of code word search requests is possible through a network of data banks and teletype communication stations.

Retrospective search of past literature has received little attention outside of taxonomic circles except through the use of available abstracts. Undoubtedly this kind of output will continue to receive slight attention due to the high cost and low user demand. The system designers must arbitrarily set a limit of usefulness for this kind of service, as shown in the previous discussion of the percentage of retrieval.

It is important to know not only what is available, but where it may be obtained. Thus, one form of output may include reference to library resources. Others may indicate the location of specimens and unpublished data.

Information from the taxonomic data file is one of the easiest kinds of retrieval systems to use because the long established system of binominal nomenclature and classification system of categories provides a logical arrangement of all taxonomic data.

Test of the Prototype.—With the prototype IRS ready for operation test the design with an index of a minimum of 1,000 to 2,000 documents. This will require a form for recording the information to be put into the system. It is assumed that thought has been given to the hardware configuration, costs, and the capacity of the file. Although it is impossible at the present time to design a single system that will be compatible with other systems for possible future tie-in, existing systems should be studied and an attempt made to design the new system so that future tie-in is possible. The specifications for processing documents will provide for the editing of titles and coding, size of storage, requirements for search and retrieval, and the format of the output. A functioning system needs provisions for up-dating, additions, and deletions.

The prototype system may be tested as soon as the information bank is stocked and a search procedure is designed. The information output may have one of the following four characteristics: 1) bibliographic references only; 2) annotated references; 3) abstracts with references, and these may be either indicative, i.e., describes the contents only, or informative, i.e., reports actual information; and 4) actual data output reported in the original documents.

Several forms of output or retrieval products of the IRS are possible. Machine printouts are the most common. Other retrieval forms are described throughout this text.

Search requests under ordinary circumstances might be by mail, using a suitable form to supply the request terms, with replies by the same method. Phone or teletype hook-up is desirable and possible when funds and user volume permits.

An important part of the system design is the plan for the processing of inquiries. The time expended on each search request, the usefulness of the output, and the volume of requests all must harmonize.

The advertising of the service should not be overlooked in the planning of an IRS. The system cannot operate without a large volume of users. It is often difficult to reach the proper persons to secure an order for these services. Every means possible, particularly society membership mailings and journal announcements should be used to attract attention to the services (SATCOM recommendation B16).

Quality control.—Once all factors have been accounted for in the design and operation of the prototype, a system of quality control is planned. This is accomplished by means of sample evaluation. Certain source documents are critically examined by the designer and then search requests are made to ascertain the quality of the output compared with the known possibilities (SATCOM recommendation B15).

System revision.—The results from the preliminary operation of the prototype should be a sufficient test of the system so that any necessary revisions may be made before the final system is put into full operation.

Final establishment of an IRS.—If a proposal based on the prototype operation of a retrieval system is submitted and a permanent system is funded, it will then be necessary to stimulate user interest. The advantages soon should be apparent. However, continuous quality control will be necessary. A review of the objectives and a test of the output in terms of these objectives will be needed at frequent intervals.

CHARACTERISTICS OF AN INFORMATION CENTER FOR DISCIPLINE ORIENTED ENTOMOLOGISTS

To stimulate interest in the use of IRS services, their characteristics must be obvious. The hoped-for features are listed below. Even more

---

CHARACTERISTICS OF AN IRS

Compact code index
Immediate access to useful information
Selection and discrimination of data as needed by user
Printed output of detailed data as required

---

service is possible. For example, a system might be established for the use of taxonomists. They might like to be able to call for the following information: 1) keys to the genera and species of a particular area as print-outs, or keys that are being revised as new information becomes available to the system; 2) a list of the species known to occur in a certain area or a certain range; 3) the range of any species included in the system; 4) a list of specific localities including the type locality; 5) habitat and host information; 6) life history data; 7) chromosome counts; 8) evolution of the group, i.e., origin and relationship of the group, etc. The many variations of these kinds of data storage, and the agreement on a useful system remain problems to be solved.

ASSIGNMENT 1 (Cont.)

1.4 Visit a nearby computer center and identify the various components. Relate their use to the IRS diagrammed (Figure 3).

1.5 Describe briefly ways an EDP-IRS could aid you in your study and research.

WHAT IS AVAILABLE FOR ENTOMOLOGICAL INFORMATION RETRIEVAL

The objectives of the Special Committee on Information Retrieval of the Entomological Society of America to establish "a truly effective storage and retrieval system for entomological literature" (Foote, 1968 and Foote and Hammack, 1969) and the activity of this committee is an indication of things soon to come. The dream is to have each laboratory provided with a desk console to search the major libraries of North America for information. Instead of going to these libraries, one could obtain information and/or citations by writing two terms, a name, or various combinations, on an electronic pad. Within a matter of minutes the text of the references selected will be thrown on a screen for rapid scanning and with the touch of a switch, they will be printed out in full for temporary file and further reference in the working library of the laboratory. Under such a system permanent files would only use valuable space that might be better occupied by other materials. This is not theoretical; similar systems are already in operation in industry and in medicine.

At the present time only very small, and perhaps ineffective, systems are in operation in entomology. These could certainly be strengthened by forming a network of discipline oriented information centers providing for the reciprocal exchange of information.

Real progress has been made at the time of this writing in several ways. Round table discussions have been held in Columbus (1968), Burlington (1969), and Bloomington (1970) to compare mutually shared problems across many scientific fields. This has aided in the future design of an entomological IRS.

In addition to the concern of the Entomological Society of America, several other organizations are interested in the developments of the entomological IRS and have helped in the planning. They are, in particular, the Biological Sciences Information Service of Biological Ab-

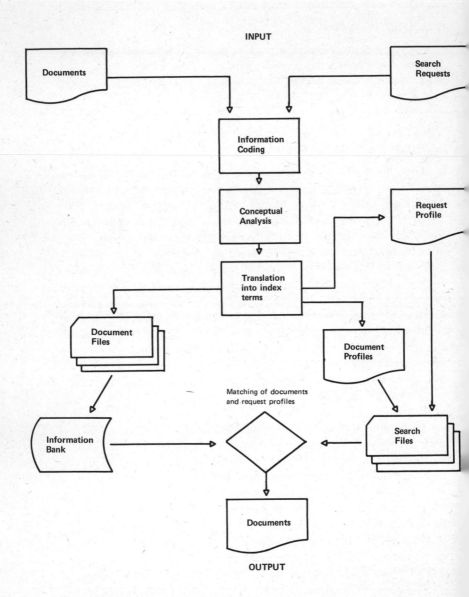

Fig. 3. An information retrieval system flowchart. See text for detailed discussion of each stage.

stracts, the Biological Communications Center Project of George Washington University, the National Academy of Sciences Council on Biological Science Information, and the National Science Foundation Office of Science Information Service.

OPTIONAL INVESTIGATION

After reviewing this chapter, write a brief description of the IRS facility you feel would be ideal for an Entomological Information Retrieval Service.

REVIEW CHECKLIST

1. Define the terms printed in italics in chapter 2. Check your definitions with those given in the glossary.
2. What are two advantages of electronic data processing (EDP) over the current methods of handling literature?
3. What are two limiting factors in the establishment of an information bank?
4. Name at least one limitation of an EDP system.
5. Give at least five common forms of information storage.
6. What are the four stages in the processing of any kind of information or data? How does this compare with the scientific method?
7. What are the advantages of the system design procedure?
8. What characteristics should an objective have? What is meant by alternate systems?
9. What criteria might be used to evaluate a system?
10. How does the evaluation of each system lead to a repetition of the analysis cycle?
11. What two factors must be balanced in coordinating the phases of a system?
12. Name the first step in the design of an IRS. Give two **ways** the information needed to achieve this may be acquired.
13. What are the advantages of a prototype IRS?
14. List several possible search file characteristics.
15. Why is it difficult to achieve 100% retrieval?
16. When is 100% retrieval necessary? When is it possible?
17. Name at least two standard coding procedures.
18. What characteristics should a code have?
19. Why is it necessary to code?
20. What characteristics should a retrieval procedure have?
21. What is meant by quality control of an IRS? Name some stages needing quality control.

22. What desirable features should the output of the IRS have?

23. List some of the particular needs of entomologists for an IRS.

CHAPTER 3

STORED INFORMATION

Stored information is any knowledge placed on record for the use of one or more persons. These deposits are known as information banks, of which there are many kinds. Some are relatively easy to use and the retrieved information forms the basis of all study, research, and development. Entomologists have two, and often three or more main information storage. They have a personal library of reference books. Their notebooks with unpublished data are used as another information bank. Very often a personal file of 3 x 5 (or another size) cards forms an information source of considerable usefulness. More recently, many research entomologists have developed a private file of key sort, or punch cards. Each of these IRS may be well organized permanent files or they may be relatively disorganized according to the needs and inclination of the user.

Information is a by-product of communication. Prior to *writing*, information was stored only in the heads of the people communicating with each other and was passed on by transitory sounds or body signs. Scratching in the dirt, then on rocks soon lead to other means of storing information. The first preserved signs and symbols were the first primitive information storage and retrieval systems. A durable packet of information that is communicated forms an information bank. It is here that records are kept.

The kinds of durable records available to man at the present time are rather limited. Some are better suited for electronic data processing than others; there must be some preliminary treatment in some way to prepare it for EDP. All known primary information packets are listed on the following table.

KINDS OF RECORDS

Handwritten documents or manuscripts
Typescripts and other forms of mechanical writing including
    printing
Drawings
Photographs, including movies and video tape
Sound recordings
Instrument tracings
Collections of specimens

The information recorded in each of these packets may be directly retrieved, that is, each is labelled for identification and they are used as needed with 100% retrieval each time they are examined. In other words the entire record must be handled each time it is used.

The records may be further prepared and stored in more formal ways. Each type of information storage has its own characteristics, but they may be classified in the manner shown in the table on the next page. Each type is discussed in this and following chapters in this book.

BOOKS

Printed books are a different form of communication. They are in a very real sense a storage and retrieval system, but they do not use EDP, i.e., there is "no hum, no click, and no blinking lights." They are, however, the first real teaching machine used by man, and they do have printed circuits! Their 500-year history has resulted in the greatest progress of man's learning. They have formed the connecting link between minds, bridging both time and space. Now, however, they are rapidly being replaced by new communication devices. Books will be with us for some time to come, but as a decreasing force in our lives. Reference works and recreation reading may continue to be produced in book form for many years, but eventually they will be replaced. The time may come when a written language using symbols as we know them will disappear. The need for faster communication devices for learning is painfully apparent. Speed reading courses

---

CLASSIFICATION OF INFORMATION STORAGE TYPES

1. E DP stored records
2. Library stored records
   2.1 Original documents
      2.11 Original data books
      2.12 Taxonomic research reports
      2.13 Experimental data
      2.14 Techniques and procedures
      2.15 Data documents
      2.16 Series
      2.17 Serials
      2.18 Films and photographs
      2.19 Maps and gazetteers
      2.20 Tapes and discs
   2.2 Information code
   2.3 Search resources
   2.4 Abstracts and indexes
   2.5 Synthesized information
      2.51 Review of taxonomic groups
      2.52 Revision of taxonomic groups
      2.53 Monographs of taxonomic groups
      2.54 Introductory textbooks and teaching aids
      2.55 Specialized textbooks and references
      2.56 Current status publications
      2.57 Taxonomic catalogs and regional lists
      2.58 Handbooks, manuals, regional works
   2.6 Popular literature
   2.7 Information on societies, institutions, organizations, and personnel
3. Museum collections
   3.1 Specimens as stored records
   3.2 Label data

---

abound, and still reading is apt to put the reader to sleep even faster than the pills he needs to quiet him as a result of his speed reading. There are many possible ways for the replacement of textbooks the same as office ledgers have been replaced. Storage in the form of video tapes, for example, has great possibilities. It is claimed that our children learn as much from television before they enter school as their parents knew by the time they entered seventh grade. This should be an encouragement to use more of this medium. In spite of this, however, books remain our most common information retrieval system.

For all retrieval systems, the coding of information is critical to its operation. In the case of a book coding is done by means of the title, the table of contents, the chapter headings, and the index. This simple retrieval system has five information portals, the four code systems, and the entire contents. Only by reading the entire book can one be certain that 100% retrieval is obtained. The same might be said of all IRS.

SPECIMENS

Entomological information input consists of documents generated from specimens and associated label data, observational and experimental data gathered with the specimens, and published information compiled from these data. The raw data of insect taxonomy are taken from insect specimens. Preserved specimens stored in collections are equivalent to stored information documents because at any time certain kinds of information may be retrieved from them. They are a part of the entomologist's information bank. Unfortunately there are certain procedural errors that persist (Arnett, 1969a) because of the confusion of insect specimens as information sources with those specimens used in museum displays. This accounts for the continued storage of pinned specimens when in most cases (Lepidoptera are a noted exception) liquid preserved material would do as well, would be more economical to store, and for many purposes would make better research material.

PHOTOGRAPHS, SOUND RECORDINGS,
AND INSTRUMENT TRACINGS

Photographs as a source of recorded data are generally ignored. Few attempts have been made to index the retrievable information stored in a photograph. At best, a caption is indexed in a file system. So unless the photograph is printed in a serial publication or in a book, the efficiency of its retrieval is very low. This is a sad commentary on our belief in the old saying that a picture is worth 10,000 words. More attention should be, and perhaps will be given to this matter. As computerized pattern recognition techniques are perfected photographs may be mechanically searched for information. In fact, this is being done now in the field of medicine.

Special files of tape recordings of insect sounds are found in only a very few laboratories. The records may be analyzed by audiospectrographs or similar equipment, but the same difficulties of coding and filing are inherent in this medium as in photographs. An alpha-numeric system for classification of recordings has been developed for library use (see bibliography).

Instrument tracings form the raw data from the insect physiology laboratory. Level recorder tapes and similar graphic displays can be transformed into data bits for computer processing. The results may be stored for retrieval as is done with other information sources.

ASSIGNMENT 2

2.1 List the kinds of IRS you maintain yourself and briefly describe the input.

STORAGE FOR MANUAL SEARCH

Storage materials are designed for two search methods. Those described previously are arranged for manual search. Others are prepared, using special storage materials, for machine search.

The reason we outline and use various headings and subheadings in *typescripts* ("*manuscripts*" are now generally typescripts) is to organize these not only for logical sequence, but as a retrieval device. Typescripts may be sorted and stored without, or with very limited, duplication (i.e., carbon copies or photocopies). As the EDP system becomes more generally available, it will be possible to store and retrieve from typescripts with the same or even greater ease than now possible from journal articles. Many technical reports are currently being published only in abstract form, so the system is already used in some fields. Libraries often have a manuscript collection; usually, however, it is of material of historical interest rather than one of current documents.

Photographs are records of many kinds of information. For example, they may be records of ecological features of a locality. Like insect specimens, photographs may be stored for later study. So far, the only coding system for photographs requires manual retrieval and visual study. There is described in chapter 6 of this text a method of indexing photographs.

In the early years after World War II photocopying machines were crude, but with the perfection of *xerography,* exact copies of documents of all kinds except photographs may be made easily and economically. This puts all old, non-copyrighted articles and books, including those long out of print and scarce, within reach of even the smallest library. It is possible, in a matter of seconds, to phone documents from city to city from library to an office or laboratory. Any reference stored in one library may be transmitted to another in this manner so that the need for interlibrary loans and the risks involved may be eliminated. In fact, it may prove to be more economical to supply users with photocopies of all reference material rather than to remove the books from the library on loan of any sort.

File cards and file cabinets remain a standard means for storing information. For limited use, file cards continue to be an efficient and ready means for information retrieval. Because the system is so easy to use, there are many millions of cards prepared, stored, but are seldom used. The owners do not give careful thought to the requirements of an 3 x 5 card file IRS. One must apply the same principles to the storage and retrieval of information on cards as to any other system.

File cards are most efficiently used for storing information for a short time. Usually the life of the system need not extend beyond the time necessary to complete a particular project [up to 3 years seems to be standard]. If the file is intended for use for a longer period of time then it is better to use EDP. Also, if the project involves more than one or two users of the file, EDP retrieval may be more effective. Exceptions to this apply to bibliography files used by libraries, or specimen catalog files, each of which are continuously being added to over long periods of time.

Each file starts with the *orientation card* which describes the purpose and extent of the file and the source of the information actually included. Each time more information is added to the file, the source is noted on the orientation card. For example, a bibliographic file that is compiled with the use of *Biological Abstracts* should tell what issues of that journal have been consulted. As new issues appear and are checked, this fact is noted on the orientation card. The notation is made even if no reference is added to the file; this prevents checking the same issue more than once. The orientation card can be consulted at any time to see if a particular source has been checked.

The amount of information that needs to be included on each card in the file determines the size of the card to select. An universal size is 3 x 5 inches. When a larger card is necessary, perhaps the card file should be replaced by a notebook system. File cards larger than 3 x 5 are used for recording special data and are not considered further here because the purpose of this discussion is to explain the nature of this medium for use in information retrieval.

Many weights and colors of cards are available. The use of colored cards and a variety of index cards aid in visual retrieval. The tabs are an important part of the IRS coding so their use follows coding principles.

The advantages of file cards are: open end system; relatively low cost; may be prepared anywhere. Their disadvantages are: must be sorted to use; time consuming to use; generally are not compatible with other systems.

FACTORS TO CONSIDER IN FILE CARD IRS DESIGN

Amount of information to record
Size of card to use according to amount of information
Permanency of file, i.e., how long it will be useful
Indexing
Color coding
Storage
Efficiency and convenience compared with other systems

Notebook filing systems require the same planning as the file card system. The same factors apply and the only advantage over file cards is that the notebook file is generally more portable and more information may be stored on the sheet. If these are advantages, notebooks should be used.

ASSIGNMENT 2 (Cont.)

2.2 Set up a neat 3 x 5 file card system, stored in a file box, with tab cards for subjects. Use this as a means of building a bibliography on the topics discussed in this book and in your own area of interest in entomology. Refer to the "Style manual for biological journals" for the method of citing publications.

Do the same thing using a suitable looseleaf notebook, 3 ring, 8½ x 11 inches. Set up a system using dividers for note storage, a subject heading for each of the chapters contained in this book. [This may be used for storing completed assignments.]

STORAGE FOR MACHINE SEARCH

Many different forms of machine search materials are available. No attempt is made to discuss each of them here. Those interested will need to make a special study of the literature supplied by the manufacturer and to consult with specialists on information retrieval. A few of the common devices available to everyone are described below.

Microfilm provides a combination of compact storage and mechanical retrieval. Documents are photographed on 35 mm film, usually two pages per frame. The great reduction of the page size permits a more compact storage size but is less convenient to use because of the need for a special reader. The film document is placed in the reader and the pages are scanned by projection onto a viewing screen. If copies of certain pages are desired, these may be printed by using a special attachment to the reader. Refinements of this basic system make use of smaller size film stored in a special cassette which is placed in a machine reader. By a keyboard selector, specific pages may be rapidly located. Microfilm sets of entire runs of journals are conveniently stored by this means with the combined advantages of compact size and rapid retrieval.

Microcards are prints made from microfilm or microfiche for use with a handlens or low power microscope as a reader.

Microfiche is similar to microfilm except that the documents are photographically printed on small transparent cards, many pages per card. These are then indexed and stored in the same manner as file cards. A microfiche reader is necessary for their use as with microfilm.

Key sort cards are a widely used and basic IRS using mechanical means for retrieval. Their two main advantages are that they are open-end retrieval, i.e., may be added to and used in many different ways at any time, and they need not be sorted before use. This system is an open-end tool because the coding permits a single data card to be retrieved through the use of many different subject heads and additional headings may be coded and added to the card at any time.

Indexing of key sort cards (figure 4) is accomplished by punching out a triangular slit in the side of a card to open one of the regularly placed holes. Although there are many sizes and arrangements of key sort cards available, all use the same basic principle of retrieving a card from the deck. By means of a notch it will fall out of the deck when the sorting rod is inserted through a particular hole in the deck of cards.

The information to be recorded is written or typed directly onto the cards. More than one card may be used if more space is needed and provision is made to code the sets as well as the subjects. Some users have special forms printed onto the cards and the code system is indicated on the form. This is the best way to use this system.

Before the system is started, the code to be used is planned and recorded as a guide both in building and in using the deck. There are two ways to code the cards. One makes use of each hole as a separate, consecutively numbered item. The numbered holes are in reverse order around the card with left side, right side, and bottom distinguished. Note, however, the correct position of the card in the deck is determined by the cut upper right hand margin. All cards are aligned in this manner. Some cards may be obtained with a double row of holes along each side. A shallow notch will retrieve an item coded to the outer row and a deep notch, those in the inner row. The second method greatly increases the number of items that may be coded by the simple system of using four holes to represent each digit, each block of four representing a different digit of a number. The four holes are numbers 7, 4, 2, and 1 from left to right. The digit one is obtained by notching the 1 hole, two by the 2 hole, three by the 2 and 1 hole, four by the 4 hole, five by the 4 and 1 hole, and so on through nine. Ten is obtained by notching the 1 hole in the second set of four, and none in the first set. Thus, the right hand set of four becomes the unit digit, the next left, the tens, the next left the hundreds, and so on. Large code numbers, including numbers like social security numbers and others may be easily coded. This system gives the card great versatility, but makes it more cumbersome. Several passes of the sorting rod are needed for each retrieval. A large size deck is severely limited because of this. It would soon be less time consuming to sort and tab index the cards for retrieval, duplicating the cards needed under more than one tab.

The key sort system has very limited use, and they are seldom used correctly. Their most efficient use seems to be in building a file of rather limited use over a long period of time, the data added slowly as new information becomes available. Distribution records of an insect

Fig. 4. An example of one of the many styles of Key Sort cards.

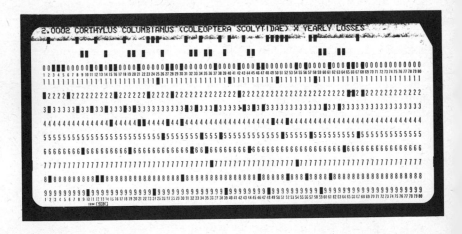

Fig. 5. A sample IBM punch card.

species might be recorded on these cards. Occassional questions about the distribution of a species within a limited area, or the names of the species that occur in an area could be answered from this kind of a file. The system has only slight advantage over an ordinary card file system. The cards are time consuming to prepare, but need not be sorted. They are more expensive than ordinary file cards. The difficulty in using them is because of the negative retrieval system, i.e., the cards that remain after each pass are not the ones desired. If a card fails to drop out of the deck, the efficiency of the system is impaired. Anyone using the system must plan to use it many times and to add continually to it. Otherwise an ordinary file card system is preferable.

A somewhat more mechanical storage system is a complex system termed *"optical coincidence system."* One of these, the Termatrex, employs a record sheet representing a word listed in a thesaurus prepared for the system. Documents are numbered consecutively and coded. The thesaurus sheet has a hole accurately bored into it by the preparator. This represents the number of the document to be stored. The hole is placed on a coordinate and may be read by crossing lines running to each margin. To find the articles containing information on certain topics, the thesaurus sheets are placed one on top of the other over a light table. The numbers of the documents are retrieved by reading those numbers shown to be coincident by the light passing through the holes in the sheets and the numbers read on the coordinates. The document is then located in the file by the number.

Although this system is widely used and it has a fairly large capacity, there seems to be little advantage to the system. Preparation is involved and retrieval complicated.

Punch cards (figure 5) are by far the most generally used for machine (ADP and EDP) retrieval. These cards have 80 positions representing units or characters which may be machine read by 1 or 0 positions on the 12 banks or positions for each unit. This coding is standardized for the EDP machines and is universally accepted. A key punch machine similar to a typewriter is used to punch the cards. Computer programs are available or can be designed to automatically read and retrieve the cards. The details of this system, as has been pointed out previously, are beyond the scope of this book. Some further details are to be found, however, in the next chapter.

While punch cards are the simplest and most generally used method of input for IRS using ADP, there are other methods. For example, a *paper tape* may be punched. These tapes are used for many purposes (for example, a short piece of this tape may be found in check book order forms and is used to set type automatically for the printing of the name, check number, and account numbers, on the checks). These tapes are prepared on a keyboard as a continuous tape but they are used much the same as punch cards. The tape has many special purposes, but is generally not used for the type of information retrieval described in this book.

The need for punch cards is eliminated by the use of a teletype *terminal* which is available for "on-line" access to the computer. Equipped with a standard typewriter keyboard, the terminal permits the storage of information directly on tape. Direct access to the computer is possible, so that, in effect, the terminal becomes a remote communication channel to the computer. Data are supplied; the program processes the data as questions are posed; answers are received in a matter of seconds. The terminal permits shared time with a computer. By operating the EDP machinery full time, cost to the individual is reduced.

Ferric tape may be used with the computer itself. Data are machine transferred from the punch cards to the tapes or placed directly on the tape from a terminal. It is passed from the tape into the computer where the retrieval operation proceeds mechanically. Furthermore, data may be permanently stored on tape, and added to as required.

The internal method of computer storage is by means of a *magnetic core* memory. These store information much as the binary digits or bits punched on the cards. The presence or absence of a bit of information determines the direction of magnetism in the core which in turn represents the information stored. Search is effected by reading this magnetic pattern. (See Evans, 1966 for details.)

Finally, the newly developed *random access data cell* or *disk pack* is a variety of the core, but has even a greater capacity than the magnetic core memory, and is much faster.

The advantages of all of these machine systems are capacity and search speed (see chapter 1). The relative costs and capacity of each is shown in the table on the following page.

RELATIVE ATTRIBUTES OF STORAGE MEDIA

	Cards	Tape	Disk
units	2000/box	2400 ft./tape	2000 tracks/pack
equivalents	1 box	160 feet	approx. 49.5 tracks
volume/unit	406 cu. in./box	113 cu. in./tape	530 cu. in./pack
advantages	cheapest	least space	fastest access
disadvantages	deteriorates fastest; most space needed	slowest access	most expensive

PROCESSING INPUT FOR INFORMATION FILE

Several kinds of information documents are prepared for storage and later retrieval. They may be grouped as: 1) current literature of *original documents*; 2) abstracts of 1 appearing as secondary information documents; 3) synthesis of 1 as *secondary literature*, and 4) taxonomic data catalogs. The latter have a unique position in entomological information retrieval and are discussed in detail elsewhere (Arnett, 1970).

In each of these kinds of documents, the process system is the same, i.e., there is a bibliographic citation involved along with one or more code words used to identify the document. Further, each must be prepared for future up-dating and possible change. Up-dating is possible only if the coding system (bibliographic citation and key words) provide a unique code for each document in such a way that no document citation added later will duplicate a previous code combination. Certain changes may be necessary at a later time, which may be provided for by adequate cross-references. This is particularly necessary for the taxonomic data catalog. The subject matter of the documents and the extent of the thesaurus will determine the exact processing procedure. Each of these is discussed in the following chapters.

Most document processing that is done by the editor or author of the document is inadequate because of the general lack of understanding of what is needed, and this will remain so until editors give authors proper instructions and until the journals' formats provide for information retrieval needs. At the present time most documents are identified by author, title, and publication. This is usually insufficient for the coder preparing material for storage and retrieval. The coder must refer back to the original document as it is published and do much of the preparation for processing by a study of the contents and the selection of descriptors or key words for an adequate document profile.

Titles of documents might very well be used for coding except that they are not consistently informative. Some titles reflect the contents very well, and others are grossly misleading. Titles are used for retrieval by *Biological Abstracts* in their permuted index, *B.A.S.I.C.* but only after enrichment by the addition of key words according to the contents of the text. All key words in the title then are used as an index word for subject retrieval by the user.

When planning the input procedure, tie-in with existing systems should be considered. For entomology, there is no net-work of functioning EDP information retrieval systems. The major search systems are abstracting services at the present time. These will be studied in detail and used when completing the assignments to follow.

SIZE OF THE INFORMATION BANK

Most of the retrievable information on entomological subjects is to be found in journals and books. The size of the information bank will depend upon the extent of the information sources and the expected use. Most private libraries and private insect collections have no need for an information bank. The user knows the extent of his holdings and goes directly to them for use. The size of a library's information bank may be determined by the extent of the file card cabinets, the record of the holdings. Insect collections as another form of an information bank usually are not indexed, but should be. As yet, there is no extensive storage of indexed entomological documents so no information bank has been produced for retrieval from these, but some attempts have been made to start this. The various information banks now in existance are widely scattered and in various forms. To retrieve stored data from these we must: 1) learn where the information banks are located; 2) develop new information banks for more efficient retrieval, and 3) be willing to work toward an EDP-IRS for entomology.

ASSIGNMENT 2 (Cont.)

2.3 Obtain a key sort set and plan a simple system of data retrieval. Select a subject of your choice and start a simple thesaurus (this will be developed later for another assignment). Find at least 10 recent publications on the subject, cite (see assignment 2.2), and key to the thesaurus. After planning the layout of the cards, prepare by notching a sample set. Use the system and demonstrate how it works.

2.4 Follow the same system for IBM punch cards as followed for the preparation of the key sort cards. You will need to refer to an IBM manual for instructions on the preparation of these. Before completing this assignment you will need to study the chapter on Search Resources. For the present, prepare citation cards only, using the same references prepared in assignment 2.3.

OPTIONAL INVESTIGATION

Visit an organization or an institution maintaining an information bank and discuss the system used with the operator. Write a short report describing the system.

REVIEW CHECKLIST

1. Define the terms printed in italics in this chapter. Compare your definition with the one given in the glossary.
2. What kinds of records are available?
3. Name two common information banks maintained by individual entomologists.
4. The essential features of any data storage system is the rapid retrieval of stored facts. Our most universal storage system at the present time is in the form of a book. Name two features common to most books that permit the rapid retrieval of stored data.
5. The two widely used methods of data storage, looseleaf notebooks and 3 x 5 cards have what important features in common?
6. What methods of coding are used in a file card information bank?
7. What method of coding is used in a taxonomic collection of specimens?
8. What are the difficulties of coding photographs? Recordings? What is done with certain instrument tracings?
9. What are the 6 factors to be considered in the design of a card file? A notebook file? How do the two differ?
10. What are the advantages of microfilm, microcard, and microfiche?
11. What is the advantage of key sort or IBM punch cards over 3 x 5 cards?

12. Discuss the design of a key sort system. A punch card system.

13. What are the advantages and disadvantages of an optical coincidence system?

14. Name some other EDP information banks.

15. What types of information documents must be processed in building an information bank?

16. What are the major current search systems?

17. How do titles vary and why are they difficult to process?

18. What determines the size of an information bank?

CHAPTER 4

ORIGINAL DOCUMENTS

The first recorded results of direct observations or experiments, when published, or otherwise made available to any interested persons, constitute the original literature on a subject. To this one must ultimately turn in order to find the origin of factual information that is found in secondary publications or cited as references in other primary publications. This has special importance in systematic entomology because valid names and descriptions of insects are selected according to their priority of publication. The rules and method of ascertaining this priority are set out in the International Code of Zoological Nomenclature. As a result of the acceptance of this code by entomologists, much of the literature searches carried out by systematic entomologists are made in order to comply with these rules and sometimes it seems that the search for data is secondary. The non-systematist is concerned with original documents only until he is able to synthesize the new developments in his particular area of interest. He then must reprocess the older literature to conform with the new findings. In this case, after the current literature is reviewed in secondary publications, the non-systematist has little further concern with these original documents.

A research project usually starts after a literature survey has been made. The survey of known facts about the particular insect or phenomenon shows where further research is needed. This applies whether one is attempting to devise a series of experiments to answer a question, to solve a practical problem, or to make a taxonomic revision of a group of insects. First one compiles a bibliography by checking the abstract references for research reports that have a bearing on the subject. The taxonomic study requires the compilation of a catalog of original descriptions. By using a card file, one is able to continuously add to the bibliography as new references are found. At the time of final report writing, this file will supply the list of literature cited.

After the literature references have been found, one must check each citation. The older literature may be difficult to interpret because of changes of the context of words since it was written. This is particularly true of taxonomic literature which may be written over two hundred years ago. Each time a deletion or addition is made in the Code, there may be further complications requiring another review of this old literature. Sometimes in solving nomenclatural problems it is necessary even to intrepet the older literature in a manner contrary to the intentions of the authors of the original papers. This accounts for some of the annoying name changes. Until we are able to program all coding problems, including taxonomic ones, and retrieve nomenclatural information by mechanical means, the chore remains a tedious one. Some knowledge of the provisions of the Code are necessary, therefore, in order to follow a considerable amount of the entomological literature.

Most original documents of research results are made available to other workers in printed form suitable for mass distribution at more or less frequent intervals. Until very recently no other means of presenting data have been widely used or accepted. The three most needed improvements of our literature resources is the development of methods of circulating data: 1) concisely stated; 2) compactly stored; and 3) fully coded for easy retrieval. This chapter is concerned with the forms of the original literature, how it is organized, and how it is classified. An understanding of this will enable the researcher to make a more thorough literature search in a much shorter time.

Considerable effort must be spent studying the forms of literature and their use. One should develop as a routine the practice of visiting the current literature section of the library. This should be done at least once a month. In order to save time and prevent reviewing a publication more than once, a record should be kept of the issues of journals and other literature examined. Interesting articles should be noted and the reference recorded on 3 x 5 file cards. This is the only way one can hope to keep current in his field.

The proper method of citing literature should be learned and used routinely. Lack of information and variation in the method of citation are the most common faults of many bibliographies. (See Conference of Biological Editors, 1964, pp. 74-82, for methods of citation.)

Reference to the classification of information storage types on page 29, 2.1 Original Documents, will provide the reader with a list of the topics covered on the following pages.

RESEARCH REPORTS—EXPERIMENTAL DATA

The results of experiments and related observations are usually published in one of our many hundreds of journals. There are approximately 750 major or core journals in entomology. No complete list of sources is available, but two partial lists are in manuscript (see Montgomery, 1967 and Laffoon, 1969) and another has been compiled for the Information Retrieval Committee report (Foote, 1969). No single library has all of these; only the major libraries have a majority of them.

Reports of experiments are published only once in these journals so the original data are available through some search method involving the citation of the author, journal, pages, and date. The type of information reported is coded either by the key words in the title or by subject matter listed in the abstract. Most reports follow a standard format: introduction and review of the literature, methods, results, discussion, conclusions, acknowledgements, and literature cited. This arrangement facilitates look-up. After these original data are made available, they are used in more condensed form in other publications (synthesized data publications) such as books, or in subsequent original reports on related subjects.

Crowded journals force editors to limit the amount of unworked data they will accept for publication. For example, a few decades ago there was room to publish complicated tables giving all details of the experiment and the data that resulted; or detailed lists of specimens studied during a taxonomic revision. Now only summaries are published, and soon, only conclusions will be allowed. Consequently, a system must be developed and put into operation which will permit rapid retrieval of these data without publication in journals. Such a system is discussed below under *Data Documents*.

RESEARCH REPORTS—TAXONOMIC

Taxonomic literature does not differ in principle from the reports of experiments. It is treated somewhat differently because of the priority requirements set fourth by the Code. The major difficulty in handling taxonomic reports is the need to store, for immediate retrieval, all documents published since 1758, and further, to maintain a carefully prepared catalog of this literature. Moreover, it is then necessary to interpret the writings of even the oldest of these authors and relate this to modern concepts of biology. Taxonomists have been able to do this effeciently for many years, and in this way there has been an IRS for taxonomy for a long time. Details of the system are discussed under coding in chapter 6. However, because complete data about organisms and their classification are available in journals and similar publications, a large volume of literature has resulted. The mere processing of this consumes a high percentage of the taxonomist's time.

The major use of the older literature is to determine the original, valid name for an organism and to establish a date of publication for priority purposes. It is usually possible to determine that a particular description is the original one, i.e., the first time the taxon was described. The original author almost always indicates that the description applies to the new taxon and is not a redescription of a previously described taxon. It is not always possible to quickly establish the date of publication. One must use the various search resources to do this, and these are available only in the larger libraries.

Most of the older insect taxa (prior to 1860) have been redescribed. The many subsequent publications must be cataloged and recorded for current use. To do this requires a study of both the literature and specimens by a taxonomist. These problems are not encountered in handling literature on experimental entomology. Only the useful needs to be referred to, and soon, even that is replaced by synthesized information publications.

The subsequent descriptions of taxa also appear in journal publications. Many are to be found in *serial* type publications as reviews or revisions. A *review* is a summary of the data on a taxon and a *revision* is a new classification of a taxon. The former may include new taxa and should include keys, but generally does not incorporate redescriptions nor lists of specimens examined. A revision, therefore, is more comprehensive with complete redescriptions and lists of specimens examined (see chapter 9 for additional discussion of this). Both kinds of documents contain original data. A third type, the *monograph*, includes many data that have been previously published and therefore is classified as synthesized information (see chapter 9).

The core literature may be checked and cataloged with relatively little difficulty. We may safely assume that all of the major entomological journals have been checked by the taxonomists and the new taxa recorded in a taxonomic catalog. Usually such major topics as life cycles, morphology, and classification are referred to in abstracting and indexing publications. Only a few groups of insects lack a basic taxonomic catalog, although many of them have never been assembled on a world basis. Therefore, for most groups and for major topics, it is necessary only to keep current as new issues of the periodicals appear.

RESEARCH REPORTS—Techniques and Procedures

Often in the course of research, either taxonomic or experimental, new techniques for gathering data or new procedures for handling data are developed. This information is worthy of publication so that others may take advantage of these discoveries, and in this sense it is original data. It should be treated as such by the core journals.

PERIPHERAL LITERATURE

The *peripheral literature*, compared with the core journals and *series*, pose entirely different problems for the entomologist. Peripheral literature includes all publications not considered to be core literature. The many thousands of biological journals, and even other science journals may contain information on insects. The percentage of retrieval from these journals is directly related to the importance of the journal to the other field. For example, if the entomological peripheral journal is a core journal for cellular physiology, the reports that are of interest to entomologists will be abstracted and coded making them available to entomologists as well as to physiologists. On the other hand, a great mass of publications sponsored by small museums and local natural history societies contain information that is seldom cataloged and is, therefore, lost to the permanent body of records. Occasionally such losses are unfortunate. Mendel's lost work is one notable example. The current literature explosion makes it necessary to deal severely with these publications. A practical approach to this is to establish a standard list of indexed periodicals and series with specified editorial policies and practices required for admission to the list. Starting dates for each might be set. Publications prior to certain dates for each field would be understood to be unindexed. Those who might have the occasion to use information published earlier than the dates establishing priority, or material to be found in unlisted publications, would be required to republish this information either in abstract form, or in full, with proper acknowledgement. If this republishing is not warranted, the data might simply be referred to by the user, who must understand that the unlisted publications are not readily available and he, therefore, must not expect them to be cataloged.

ASSIGNMENT 3

3.1 Prepare a set of 3 x 5 file cards using the proper method of citation as given in the Style Manual for Biological Journals. Also, see examples in the bibliography at the end of this text. It would be well to pick a single subject and begin a bibliography of this subject so far as this is possible at this time.

Prepare at least one card from current literature found in your library for the following:

A single author of a paper describing a new species in a core journal.

Two or more authors of a paper on the physiology of some insect.

An entomological paper published in a peripheral journal.

Check each paper for key words and write these on the upper right hand side of the card. This will be the beginning of the coding that will be used later as a sample retrieval system is planned and put into operation.

WHAT IS AVAILABLE FOR THE PUBLICATION OF ENTOMOLOGICAL RESEARCH REPORTS

Entomologists are both fortunate and unfortunate to have many *periodicals* and serials; fortunate because of the diversity of *publication* forms and frequency of issue; unfortunate because of the low number of subscribers to each causes a high cost of publication. It is easy to conceive of one giant publication resulting from the consolidation of all existing journals published in the United States. The cost per page for the production of this journal would be much less for the subscribers, but the individual's annual subscription bill would be considerably more, on the average, than the total presently spent for each of the individual subscriptions because no one attempts to subscribe to all journals. Clearly other solutions must be found. Another unfortunate aspect of the current situation is the absence of many of these publications in most libraries. Searching even the current literature soon becomes a dreary task in all but a few institutions.

The individual must select the journals he wishes to subscribe to mainly on the basis of his interest in the sponsoring society. Space does not permit comments on each of those available. However, even at the risk of extreme bias, some annotations must be made to enable one to start his study of these publications. The list that follows is intended for this purpose only and those prominent publications omitted are missing only because a similar publication was listed to serve as an example.

The following periodicals are examples of publications of general entomological interest and a sample of the core journals.

Annals of the Entomological Society of America, published by the Entomological Society of America, 4603 Calvert Road, College Park, Maryland 20740. Frequency: bimonthly; contents: general, morphological, taxonomic, ecological, and physiological entomology. This publication and the following are the largest single sources for original documents in entomology in the United States.

Journal of Economic Entomology, published by the Entomological Society of America (see above). Frequency: bimonthly; contents: data reports on insects of economic importance including rearing, chemical and biological control, and information on distribution and population density.

Canadian Entomologist, published by the Entomological Society of Canada, K. W. Neatby Building, Central Experimental Farm, Ottawa, Canada. Frequency: monthly; contents: all aspects of entomology.

Entomological News, published by the American Entomological Society, 1900 Race Street, Philadelphia, Pa. 19103. Frequency: monthly; contents: articles of general interest on all aspects of entomology.

Entomological publications specializing in taxonomy are abundant. Some of the major ones not devoted to a single order or small group of insects are:

Transactions of the American Entomological Society, published by the American Entomological Society, 1900 Race Street, Philadelphia, Pa. 19103. Frequency: quarterly to subscribers, but individual articles are delivered to some libraries and individuals as issued irregularly; contents: longer articles on the classification of specific groups of insects.

Proceedings of the Entomological Society of Washington, published by the Entomological Society of Washington, Systematic Entomology Laboratory, United States Department of Agriculture, c/o United States Museum of Natural History, Washington, D. C. 20560. Frequency: quarterly; contents: almost entirely insect taxonomy; includes insects from any place in the world.

Journal of the Kansas Entomological Society, published by the Kansas Entomological Society, Department of Entomology, Kansas State University, Manhattan, Kansas 66502. Frequency: quarterly; contents: taxonomy, morphology, and biology of insects, often restricted to central and western United States and Mexico.

Journal of the New York Entomological Society, published by the New York Entomological Society, American Museum of Natural History, 79th at Central Park West, New York, N. Y. 10024. Frequency: quarterly; contents: taxonomy, morphology, and biology of all groups of insects, mainly New World.

Pacific Insects, published by the Department of Entomology, B. P. Bishop Museum, Honolulu, Hawaii 96819. Frequency: quarterly; contents: taxonomy and biology of insects of the Pacific island region including the mainland coasts.

Pan-Pacific Entomologist, published by the Pacific Coast Entomological Society, c/o Department of Entomology, University of California, Davis, Calif. 95616. Frequency: quarterly; contents: taxonomy, morphology, and biology of insects, mainly of the New World.

Psyche, published by the Cambridge Entomology Club, c/o Biological Laboratory, Harvard University, Cambridge, Mass. 02138. Frequency: quarterly; contents: taxonomy, morphology, and biology of insects, mainly of the New World.

Some journals are concerned with special branches of entomology. A few examples follow.

Journal of Insect Physiology, published by Pergamon Press, Inc., 44-01 21st St., Long Island City, New York 11101. Frequency: monthly; contents: all aspects of insect physiology.

Journal of Medical Entomology, published by the Department of Entomology, B. P. Bishop Museum, Honolulu, Hawaii 96819. Frequency: quarterly; contents: taxonomy, biology, and control of insects of medical importance.

Mosquito News, published by the American Mosquito Control Association, P. O. Box 278, Selma, Calif. 93662. Frequency: quarterly; contents: articles on mosquitoes and mosquito control.

Still other journals are devoted to single groups of insects. Only a few of these are of wide enough interest to find support. Three examples are:

The Coleopterists' Bulletin, published by the Center for the Study of Coleoptera, Department of Entomology, Purdue University, Lafayette, Ind., 47907. Frequency: quarterly; contents: any aspect of the study of beetles except their control.

Journal of the Lepidopterists' Society, published by the Lepidopterists' Society, Peabody Museum, Yale University, New Haven, Conn. 06504. Frequency: quarterly; contents: any aspect of the study of butterflies and moths except control.

Journal of Research on the Lepidoptera, published by William Hovanitz, 1160 W. Orange Grove Ave., Arcadia, Calif. 91006. Frequency: quarterly; contents: articles on the taxonomy and biology of moths and butterflies.

As explained previously, there are many peripheral publications of importance to entomologists. Those frequently containing research reports on entomology are:

Science, published by the American Association for the Advancement of Science, 1515 Massachusetts Ave., N. W., Washington, D. C. 20005. Frequency: weekly; contents: articles and news on any aspect of science. Articles of entomological interest are usually on insect physiology or behavior.

Bioscience, published by the American Institute of Biological Sciences, 3900 Wisconsin Ave., N. W., Washington, D. C. 20016. Frequency: twice monthly: contents: articles and news on all aspects of the biological sciences. Articles on entomology are very seldom published.

Evolution, published by the Society for the Study of Evolution, c/o Department of Entomology, The University of Kansas, Lawrence, Kansas 66044. Frequency: quarterly; contents: insect articles are usually on genetics and speciation.

Ecology, published by the Duke University Press for the Ecological Society of America, Box 6697, College Station, Durham, N. C. 27708. Frequency: quarterly; contents: insect articles dealing mainly with their association with a certain habitat.

Journal of Experimental Biology, published by the Cambridge University Press, 32 East 57th Street, New York, N. Y. 10022. Frequency: bimonthly; contents: few insect articles, those on physiology or behavior.

Journal of Stored Products Research, published by Pergamon Press, Inc., 44-01 21st St., Long Island City, New York 11101. Frequency: quarterly; contents: articles on the biology, control, and classification of insect pests of stored products.

Serials are similar to journals except that they are issued irregularly and usually have only a single article per issue. Most of these are issued by museums or government agencies. Some of the largest serials are listed below.

Smithsonian Contributions to Zoology, Smithsonian Institution Press, Washington, D. C. 20560. Frequency: irregular; contents: taxonomy of animals. This publication replaced the *Proceedings of the United States National Museum* and the *Bulletin of the United States National Museum*. Many parts are devoted to insects.

United States Department of Agriculture Miscellaneous Publications, published by the United States Department of Agriculture. Frequency: irregular; contents: technical publications on any phase of agriculture including entomology.

Bulletin of the American Museum of Natural History, published by the American Museum of Natural History, 79th Street at Central Park

West, New York, N. Y. 10024. Frequency: irregular; contents: any aspect of natural history including taxonomic entomology.

University of California Publications in Entomology, University of California Press, Berkeley, Calif. 94720. Frequency: irregular; contents: general entomology, except control.

Many serial publications, although they have ceased to publish parts, are, in some branches of entomology, still widely used. However, they are difficult to survey and their contents are known to most readers through reference in the "literature cited" section of later publications. Because of their original limited distribution, they are difficult to find. One example is:

Bulletin of the Lloyd Library of Botany, Pharmacy and Materia Medica, Entomology Series, published by the Lloyd Library, Cincinnati, Ohio. Frequency: irregular; contents: any aspect of the taxonomy and biology of insects.

ASSIGNMENT 3 (Cont.)

3.2 Visit the library and examine a recent issue of each of the publications listed above. Make a set of 3 x 5 file cards for each of these and any other entomological journals available in the library that are of interest to you. On each card list on the upper right hand corner the card catalog number. Below the title list the extent of the library holdings of the series, i.e., volumes and dates of the issues available in the library (e. g., vol. 1, 1890 to date; or vol. 17, 1907 to vol. 27, 1917, etc.). Check the current issue of each journal and record its date on the card below the holdings reference. Make a file card for at least one article in the current issue of each journal if there is an article on the subject of your special interest.

BOOKS

Books as original documents are uncommon because they are ordinarily *current status publications* (see Synthesized Information, chapter 9), monographs, textbooks, manuals, and similar reference works. Occasionally original data are published in book form. A few examples are listed in the bibliography.

A series differs from a serial primarily because it is of a definite size and has a definite goal for completion. Some large works or monographs are issued in parts for a period of years. Two examples of series still being written and published are listed in the bibliography. Each of these will cease as soon as the projected volumes have been completed.

ASSIGNMENT 3 (Cont.)

3.3 Prepare a set of 3 x 5 file cards as in assignment 3.1 for the following:

A book published by a commercial publishing company

A book published by a governmental agency

A separate section of a book written by an author other than the editor

An example of a series

PAMPHLETS AND DIRECTORIES

The distinction between a pamphlet and a book is vague. Usually a pamphlet lacks a hard bound cover, but even this distinction is nebulous because so many books are issued either cloth bound or as paperbacks. The distinction we wish to make here is concerned with the difficulty of locating these publications. Both pamphlets containing original information and directories containing information needed to locate research materials have certain features in common. First, they are not a part of a continuing periodical or a series. Secondly, they are not published by a commercial publisher and therefore are not listed in the usual search sources. Very often they are distributed without charge by a federal governmental or state agency, a university, or a commercial manufacturing or service organization. The percentage of retrieval of publications of this nature is very low. Only a few examples are given in the bibliography (see chapters 10 and 11).

FILMS AND PHOTOGRAPHS

As previously stated movies and photographic prints store vast amounts of data, most of which cannot be searched for and retrieved. This information bank might easily be cataloged and made available through standard search resources. Some examples of films of original research known to exist are:

Photographs of type localities of North American Coleoptera, in the files of this author.

Wasp Behavior Movies, by Howard E. Evans, Harvard University. [No provision is known to have been made to make these data available to specialists except as published by Dr. Evans; this is cited here as an example only and readers should not infer that these data will be or could be made available to the public.]

Photographs of forest and grassland localities, United States Forest Service. A file of photographs by states and territories is maintained by the Forest Service in Washington, D.C. By special arrangement these photographs may be examined by biologists.

MAPS AND GAZETTEERS

Except for bound atlases, maps of many kinds are widely scattered and difficult to retrieve. The search for the location of political and geographical collecting sites by entomologists (generally taxonomists) is often time consuming. The usual commercial atlas does not contain enough detail to provide the user with the data he needs. Generally the taxonomist needs to find obscure localities recorded on insect pin data labels. The exact location of these places enables him to retrieve certain facts about the distribution of populations and species. The search resources for these data may be found through the use of geographical literature. Atlases and gazetteers as search resources are listed in the bibliography. Some examples of map resources are:

U. S. Geological Survey Maps. This is the largest collection of un-assembled maps of the United States.

American Geographical Society maps of South America. A large collection of unassembled maps published by the American Geographical Society, Broadway at 156th Street, New York, N. Y. 10028.

ASSIGNMENT 3 (Cont.)

3.4 Some places are easily found on available maps. Others demand special maps. The following list are examples of localities used on insect pin data labels. Locate and give the altitude and county or province of each of these places. Cite the reference to the map you consulted.

Rio Hato, Panama; Lambayeque, Peru; Puerto Baquerizo, Galapagos; Strawberry Mt., Oregon; Bergen, New York; Falcon Dam, Texas; Willis, Oklahoma.

OPTIONAL INVESTIGATION

The following list of places also appears on insect locality data labels, but are not readily found on maps. Find as many of these as possible and cite as for the places in the above list.

Tabernilla, Panama; Otra Lado, Panama; San Jose, Galapagos; Samborodon, Ecuador; Jame, Mexico; Pena Blanca, Arizona; Stovepipe Wells, California; Bergen Swamp, New York.

Make your own list of localities that you might use when collecting in familiar surroundings (e.g., around your home town). How many of these can you find on a map?

TAPES

It was explained previously that sound tapes are not indexed or coded, but there are tape libraries available for use by qualified research entomologists. Those listed below are examples, not exhaustive, and in no way does this imply that these collections are available for public use.

Cornell University Laboratory of Ornithology. A large collection of insect sounds has been acquired in addition to bird songs.

University of Michigan, Department of Zoology. Tapes of songs of Orthoptera and other insects made by R. Alexander and others.

University of Florida, Department of Entomology. Recordings of Orthoptera and other insects collected by T. J. Walker and others.

Purdue University, Center for the Study of Coleoptera, Department of Entomology. A tape library of stridulatory sounds of beetles recorded by Eileen R. Van Tassell and R. H. Arnett, Jr.

For additional sound recordings of insects, see commercial catalogs, especially *Folkways Records, 165 W. 46th St., New York, NY 10036.*

DATA DOCUMENTS

The scientific and technical communication bottleneck is recognized as a pressing national problem by the National Academy of Sciences and the National Academy of Engineering (the SATCOM report points this out). Yet many inexpensive means for the solution of this problem are immediately available (Arnett, 1970). One solution lies in selectively disseminated publication (*selective dissemination of information*

(SDI), see SATCOM recommendation C 12). This method of publication is already in use in several fields. For entomology, one such
system is currently in operation on a small scale. This is described
below.

"Data Documents for Systematic Entomology (DDSE)" is a new
publication concept for the rapid communication of data without
publication in the usual sense. The principles of publication are the
same, i.e., *duplication* and distribution. In the belief that most taxonomic data reported as the result of original research is of direct interest to only a few specialists, and that these data should be available
almost immediately to this group, the new concept was proposed. No
doubt within a very short time many journals as we know them will
cease to exist. Data will be stored for instant retrieval in national or
international data processing centers. Journals will then convert to become current awareness media and a source for synthesized information. Emphasize will be placed on serving subscribers with useful information and less on their archival storage function.

Data Documents are processed in exactly the same manner as any
typescript. Illustrations are prepared as if for printing and publication
in the traditional manner. The document is submitted to a Data
Document Center through a journal and its editorial board. The same
reviewing and editing follows, including marking for the printer. Format inconsistencies are corrected, an informative abstract prepared, and
descriptors listed. Upon receipt, the document is given a file or document number, which to a certain extent indicates the nature of the
document, i.e., the numbers are coded to serve as a cross reference in
handling the documents. Once this process has been completed, the
document is set in type and page proof prepared for reproduction by
xerography or offset. Copies (3 or 4) are sent to appropriate Data
Document centers to assure the preservation of the data. It is emphasized that all libraries and individuals are not to accumulate sets of
these documents. This would defeat the entire purpose of the procedure. The general-use data or information is made available in review,
revision, monograph, or synthesized form. Information stored as Data
Documents is of use and interest to only a few individuals and should
receive only that amount of distribution. Libraries may act as Data
Document centers if they wish and have the space. Some laboratories
also require complete sets for their daily work. This is provided for,
and is within the concept that Data Documents is meant to provide

data where it is needed, when it is needed, as rapidly as possible. This eliminates the need to store several thousand copies indefinitely unused. Authors are supplied with a limited number of copies which may be used as "reprints".

The parent information center storing Data Documents produces two types of current awareness notices for publication in the sponsoring journal. One consists of the title and the descriptors. A reference is given to the complete document, and where it may be obtained. This method is used for documents listing insect pin label data, or reporting similar raw data. The second type includes, in addition, an informative abstract. If new taxa are described in the Data Document, a diagnosis, or brief description, is published for each taxon to validate the new names. The parent periodical is sent to the entire mailing list as usual. It is not anticipated that the journal will convert entirely to Data Documents; it will include articles of general interest as well as other information such as news items and announcements. The complete Data Document may be ordered from the Data Document center by mail, telephone, or, as the system develops, by telecopier terminal. These documents are reproduced by what ever method is appropriate to meet the needs of those interested. Illustrations are duplicated without loss of fidelity.

Data Documents are available to the user as rapidly as the awareness journal appears. If monthly, then they are published with a maximum waiting period of a month, plus the time it takes to prepare and mail the journal, and the time needed to order and return documents. At its slowest, it is more rapid than conventional means of publication, and the document never goes out of print.

ADVANTAGES OF DATA DOCUMENTS

Speed of information dissemination
Economy of space required to store entire issue of publication
Economy of production of journals
Readily available copies anytime—never "out of print"
Limited, but effective, circulation

DISADVANTAGES OF DATA DOCUMENTS

High cost of individual copies and resulting lack of wide reprint circulation to those who will never use the document

The elimination of the "browsing" aspects possible with current journals
Production of still another information source

The advantages of Data Documents seem apparent. The system meets present demands for space economy and the limited but effective circulation conserves user's time.

The apparent disadvantages are greatly outweighed by the advantages. The high cost of individual articles is more than balanced by the reduced expense for journal subscriptions. Even with the disappearance of the publication of raw data, periodicals will continue as synthesis publications and will be widely circulated. The permanence of copies is assured by the deposit of master copies in at least three Information Centers. This will assure also that the terms of the Code are met, i.e., the documents are not privately circulated. "Browsing" actually can be enhanced because more time can be spent reading synthesis articles and noting the Data Documents in the references cited. Except that the method of presentation of data may be missed, wider coverage of the literature is possible for any individual through the use of the system, and of course there are other ways to learn how to present data. The matter of libraries subscribing to the entire series of documents and thus defeating one of the prime purposes of Data Documents —that of saving space occupied by archival material is easily handled by instructing librarians and inviting them to participate in the program. Once librarians understand the advantages of the system, and perhaps agree to the establishment of Data Document centers in their institutions, the program will be accepted.

In summary, Data Documents is essentially a refinement and wider application of the same system used by Dissertation Abstracts for theses. The xerox printout of the microfilmed thesis meets all of the requirements of publication and the republication of this material is redundant. The printouts are "printed", bound, and widely circulated by subscription. A thesis should be prepared for final publication and treated as such when it becomes available in the form used by Dissertion Abstracts.

Data Documents are currently produced by the American Entomological Society with the parent journal, *Entomological News*. Information centers are planned as the depository for the documents and the retrieval services.

INSECT SPECIMENS

Previous reference was made to preserved insect specimens as a source of data, and as stored specimens they may supply the information for new documents at anytime. This need to store information in this manner greatly affects the methods and procedure of entomologists and other biologists and creates many different problems for these scientists not comparable to the processing of information in other branches of knowledge. For example, the physist and chemist deal only with species of things because there is no individual variation. They are able to make precise predictions about the behavior of these materials. Thus they have no need to store individuals. Conversely, artists deal only with unique individual objects, so their information storage poses still different problems. Because many phases of biology, including taxonomic entomology, are concerned with variation and comparative data, the storage of specimens, as samples, is required.

Errors in labelling, distortions through preservation, and lack of detailed data associated with the specimens, contribute some of the inaccuracies found in systematic information records. An awareness of this will serve to improve the recording of data in the future as well as to help the proper handling of existing information. Because of the requirements of the Code, taxonomists are prone to publish too much information too quickly, well before it has been processed sufficiently for use by others. Therefore, a large amount of erroneous information may be passed from publication to publication as fact, for the Code has no article that requires that published information be demonstrable as fact! A statement printed on a locality data label and attached to a specimen is not sufficient evidence of data validity, but it may provide information suitable for storage as Data Documents.

The scientific method requires that observations and experiments be repeatable. This means that, barring catastrophies of nature and man, samples of extant species, and information associated with these samples can be obtained again by anyone whenever the proper circumstances are present. Failure to gather these data does not necessarily invalidate the original data. It may mean, however, that the original information was too scanty to meet scientific requirements. The time now has come for the development of a set of standards for acceptable specimens and associated data. Specimens not meeting these standards should be disregarded except under unusual circumstances.

Single specimens in a collection are either correctly or incorrectly labelled. Series of specimens bearing exactly the same label data may be incorrectly labelled. With the collection of two or more specimens in a single locality, one fact is established: some morphological variation of the species. When still more samples have been gathered in the same locality by the same person or different persons at other times or during the same season of other years, the chance of both samples having been incorrectly labelled is insignificant. Once the same species has been collected at other localities, the validity of the theory of the existence of the species is established.

Traditionally, collecting is a random but biased procedure. Seldom has the taxonomic entomologist set out in advance to discover the distribution of a population or a species. This is, like labelling, another weak part of our information gathering system because we are willing to accept the data we have. We grasp these meager data and rush them to the printer to be recorded as a taxonomic "first" without consideration of their true significance! Carefully planned collecting would improve even the first stages of taxonomy.

From the input information associated with the proper species, detailed records of host, habitat, and habits for each sample may add valuable data to show variations within a single population: seasonal, genetic, environmental, and other variation.

Habitat descriptions that include weather data, altitude, slope, vegetation, and other information about the effective environment may be useful for the specimens collected at the time of the visit, and for the association of other collections made at other times when these details were not needed.

Information output is reused, added to, and stored back into the system. It is superfluous to say that the proper association of data and species is of paramount importance to the success of any information storage and retrieval system. It is not superfluous to emphasize that the only purpose of the Code is to provide an efficient program for the formation of names to be used as index terms for the storage and retrieval of this information. Once a less cumbersome system has been devised, the Code is obsolete. Such a system is at least theoretically possible, so the Code is at least theoretically obsolete. We should work to develop a new system before someone else does it for use.

Storage and retrieval of insect specimens as information documents can be easily and cheaply programmed. Several programs are now available, and the same one used for literature retrieval described in a later chapter may be easily adapted to this purpose. We could formalize a program for insect label data, but only when some general agreement has been reached by a large body of our taxonomists. The trouble in the past has been in attempting to establish absolute priority for names, and thereby implying that 100% retrieval has been achieved. The Code has only recently relaxed this requirement by providing for the use of some names that may not be the oldest for the species, with no effect on the efficiency of the retrieval.

Many branches of biology have been able to quantify working data through the use of various measuring and recording instruments. Little attempt has been made to do the same for data associated with insect specimens. Although insect collections still bear the classical three-line data label—the place, the date, and the collector's name, some improvement has been made by a majority of collectors since the early 1940's. They have been careful to record localities more precisely, and most have included information that might be termed "ecological", but little else. Because of the priority requirements of the Code, specimens have "historical" value, so most specimens, once information about them has been recorded in print, must be kept regardless of their condition or sparsity of data. In spite of the logic behind this need for data, many state university collections still accept specimens with nothing more than a county label, no doubt due to the practice of making crop surveys and reporting the results by county.

Storage of undigested raw data as printed matter is wasteful. For example, the mere listing of locality records from insect specimen labels, arranged alphabetically or geographically, is still raw data. When printed and stored, ready for use by the next researcher, it is he who must do the actual research by interpreting as best he can the significance of the data. Lists of temperature recordings taken during some physiological experiment are comparable data and would not be published. We forget that we write primarily for the use of the non-specialist, not the one other specialist on our group. The work should be done for the user, not as a mere appraisal of the current status of our own research, but as a finished working tool. The progress reports can be better distributed to the specialists by the Data Document system. However, if a list of collecting sites is recorded, especially when it tells others the season during which to collect, what to expect, and provides information about the habitat, then a useful contribution is made.

Endless amounts of information might be gathered and prepared for storage. A simple means of storing this might be to prepare a punch card for each information class, the cards coded to species and type of information. Arranged and stored, they may be changed at any time and are available for immediate printout. The following list suggests several information classes, some of which might be further subdivided:

1. Species card with classification code.
2. Preserved specimen (as individuals) card keyed to lot records.
3. Literature reference card (for taxa).
4. Locality data card.
5. Field record card.
6. Experimental data cards.
7. Measurement (individual) card keyed to 2, above.
8. Ecological information cards (this item can be broken into many parts).
9. Photograph record card keyed to 4 and 5 above.
10. Literature reference cards for ecological data and other information.
11. Cards showing the collection in which each vouchered specimen is stored, also keyed to 2 above.

The format of these cards, and indeed, the entire system, is being studied in several laboratories (Arnett, 1967b) to devise a functional arrangement.

Unfortunately little information on associated data other than that obtained from the "standard" locality data label is readily available with most collections. Some collections, particularly those closely connected with projects of an economic nature (mission oriented), have lot record systems so that many specimens have an abundance of associated information. Without doubt a great amount of data not keyed to the specimens is available from individual collectors. If collectors would prepare these data for storage and distribution with loaned specimens, their research value would be increased greatly.

ASSIGNMENT 3 (Cont.)

3.5 Examine an insect collection and select a suitable series of specimens for study. Record those kinds of data that can be used for a system as described here.

OPTIONAL ASSIGNMENT

List the data obtained from the above assignment on 3 x 5 file cards and transfer these to IBM punch cards.

REVIEW CHECKLIST

1. Why are bibliography cards listed by author and date?
2. How can you tell whether or not an article is an original document?
3. Who is concerned with original documents?
4. Give two reasons why it is necessary to make a literature survey.
5. Name two kinds of research reports.
6. Why is taxonomic data published in its entirety?
7. Define: review, revision, monograph.
8. What is peripheral literature? Why is this difficult to retrieve?
9. Approximately how many entomological core journals are published?
10. Approximately how many are generally available?
11. What percentage of the current entomological literature do you think this represents?
12. What is the difference between a series and a periodical?
13. What three ways might lead to the improvement of our literature resources problem?
14. Name some of the several types of entomological journals available.
15. Why aren't books usually original documents? Is this book?
16. What makes pamphlets difficult to retrieve?
17. Data Documents is a new concept in publication. How is it unique?
18. Name three advantages over present methods of publication offered by the Data Document concept.
19. Name three disadvantages of the above.
20. How may insect specimens be considered "original documents"?
21. What criteria are necessary for an insect specimen to be scientifically valid as a datum source?
22. How might insect specimens be treated in an IRS?
23. Why is the reporting of insect pin label data considered to be raw data rather than synthesized data?

CHAPTER 5

PREPARATION OF ORIGINAL DOCUMENTS FOR STORAGE

Data gathering, processing, and reprocessing usually leads to some form of publication for information storage. The proper preparation of this information and the selection of the correct method of presentation is a subject of considerable complexity. It involves the author, the *editor*, and the *publisher*. All three must work closely and cooperatively for a quality product. Each has a special job to do, and one cannot work without the help of each of the others.

The author must design his product in terms that relate to the existing body of knowledge. The data that he gathers must be worked into an intelligible unit so that it may be presented to others within the context of the medium used for publication. Most of all, it must be complete in itself and not require additional work on the part of the reader to render it usable.

The editor acts as a double agent. He represents the author to the publisher and the publisher to the author. It is his job to provide the control of the quality of the publisher's product. He must be aware of the research being done in the areas of interest to the publishers of books or periodicals. He must know enough of the technology of publishing to be able to design a product compatable with the medium to be used.

The publisher is primarily concerned with the actual production of the work and its proper distribution. Both the editor and the publisher work toward an economical product with a maximum useful distribution.

This chapter is concerned primarily with the above trilogy. Figure 6 shows the various media and stages used for the dissemination of information. Many problems caused by the information explosion would be brought under control if more attention were given to this coordination.

THE AUTHOR

Many reasons may prompt a person to author a publication. Some of these are listed below:

PURPOSES SERVED BY PUBLICATION OF SCIENTIFIC PAPERS

To complete a project by making information available to others
To provide working tools for the researcher himself as well as others
To reach others performing related research
For personal satisfaction
To advertize an author's creativity
To advertize the work of an authors organization
To provide demonstration of productivity of an organization
To establish or maintain personal status
To establish or maintain institutional status

The details of paper writing are given in many books and style manuals. The discussion that follows concerns only certain features pertaining to document preparation and *format* for more efficient information retrieval that are not treated, as yet, in style books.

Titles.—Whenever possible, a title should be selected that has no more than 80 characters so that it will fit on a punch card for easy

MEDIA FOR THE DISSEMINATION OF INFORMATION

Inception of Work

Literature Search

Progress
⇓
Part, or all of the work completed
⇓

Informal and ⇓ Semiformal communication

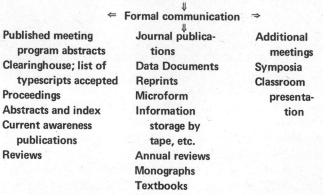

Written communications:	⇐ Reports ⇒ prepared	Oral communications:
Manuscripts	⇓	Colloquium
Copies of meeting paper	⇓	Seminar
Technical reports	⇓	Special confer- ence
Progress reports		Meeting
Technical notes and memos	⇓ Informal	presenta- tions:
Final reports	preprints	Local
	⇓	Regional
	Submitted for publication	National
		International
	⇓	
	Formal preprints	

⇓
⇐ Formal communication ⇒
⇓

Published meeting program abstracts	Journal publica- tions	Additional meetings
Clearinghouse; list of typescripts accepted	Data Documents Reprints	Symposia Classroom
Proceedings	Microform	presenta-
Abstracts and index	Information	tion
Current awareness publications	storage by tape, etc.	
Reviews	Annual reviews	
	Monographs	
	Textbooks	

Fig. 6. Chart showing possible ways information may be distributed by authors.

permutation (see chapter 6). A title may have no more than three elements: 1) name of organism or group; 2) geographical region covered, and 3) the phenomenon or processes discussed. The key words and their connectives must be carefully arranged if the title is to be kept short and at the same time be informative. One common mistake in taxonomy is to include too much detail about the classification of the group in the title, and not enough in the text. For example, there is no need to give names of the species when more than one is discussed and no need to tell that new taxa are described. New taxa are not really "new" and the establishment of priority is certainly a trivial matter compared to the true nature of the contents of such a paper, i.e., the ability to recognize a taxon. It would be more factual to say that the paper contains previously unrecognized taxa. On the other hand, the order and family is very important information but is sometimes omitted. A second fault is the omission of the geographical region covered. Some papers need to be read in detail before it becomes apparent that the group being discussed does not occur in the area of the user's interest. The inability of an author to recognize the nature of the phenomenon he has been studying may be apparent when his title is compared with his text. He may confuse zoogeography with the recording of scanty distribution data, or evolution with a discussion of a few morphological features, and similar mislabelling may occur in papers on physiology. Titles tend to be either too grandiose or record information that is too detailed. It seems that some authors think of a title, then write a paper that tries to fit the title. More attention must be given to titles in order to speed up document sorting (see chapter 6).

Abstracts.—Abstracts help in the pinpointing of document content. They should be informative, not descriptive, but should contain all key words used in coding a document. In preparation for computer scanning, an abstract of no more than 1600 *characters* should be required by all journals (see chapter 8). A separate list of code terms or descriptors should be provided, arranged alphabetically after the abstract. Compound words are acceptable and often must be used. Avoid three word codes or phrases (see chapter 5). Whenever a new term is used, this should be clearly indicated in the text of the document and in the abstract, where a brief definition also should be given. The code term should be marked "new term" in the descriptor list.

Writing. Writing of the document itself should follow the *editorial policy* of the publisher or publication to which the author plans to submit his work. Common mistakes are given here, particularly those not emphasized in writing guides.

Failure to leave adequate margins, especially at the top and on the left side for editor's *notations* is very common. The typescript should have a top margin of at least four inches on the first page and the title either on a separate sheet or adequately spaced out. Special attention should be given to the form of the by-line, i.e., the author's name and affiliation, which should follow the format used by the journal.

Never use caps or *underlining* except for foreign words or Latin names of species. Also, remember that it is logically impossible to refer to a genus without a species unless it is the generic name only as a nomenclatural word that is being referred to. Therefore, it is necessary to add "sp.' or "spp.' after a generic name, or to insert the generic name or initial in front of a specific name in all cases.

Unfortunately, much of the bad style a student learns is taught to him in his courses in English and fostered by the requirements set down in guides for thesis preparation. For example, marking of the typescript for type faces, sizes, and form should be left to the editor. *Double space* everything. Titles, by-lines, footnotes, text, quotes, captions, and literature citations must be double spaced so that the editor can mark these for the printer. Single spacing of these parts make it difficult to mark and leads the editor to believe that the author does not understand the mechanics of paper writing.

Abbreviations must be carefully selected; only use standard forms that will be recognized by all readers. As a general rule *footnotes* are to be avoided because of the extra cost for typesetting and because they are distracting to the reader. A *paragraph indentation* is always used to indicate the beginning of paragraphs. Block paragraphs are not used in text matter. *Hanging indentations* are never used for descriptions or special matter. Keys are an exception to this rule but one should be sure to follow the format used by the publication that will consider the typescript. No special characters should be used, for example, sex signs. Certain mathematical symbols must be used in formulas, but should be avoided in the text. All special symbols must be hand inserted in most machine composition, which greatly increases costs if used excessively. Certain symbols are available, as for example, those used on maps to indicate species distribution, etc., but the author should check with the publisher before these are used.

Illustrations.—The preparation of adequate *illustrations*, as with good writing, is a special topic not considered here. Most editors desire a consecutive numbering of all *figures* even when made into a series of *plates.* *Line cuts* may be handled as text matter, but the author must make sure that the lines are thick enough to withstand the amount of reduction needed for the proper page size. *Halftones* must be printed on *glossy* or *coated paper* if the publisher is using letterpress, but beautiful reproduction of halftones and even color illustrations may be done on many kinds of paper in addition to coated paper when the press-work is by offset. Unless the publication is normally printed on paper suitable for the printing of halftones, *tip-ins* will be necessary, at considerable extra cost. However, some publications do this routinely.

Prepublication review.—A document is usually reviewed before publication by the document review committee of the sponsoring institution, and by the publisher's *editorial board.* Neither group is responsible for errors of fact, which remain the author's responsibility. These *reviewers* look for ambiguity, poor organization, inconsistencies, and ways to make the paper more concise. Although their help is indispensible, and they should be acknowledged along with the technical help given by colleagues, they too have biases that may bring problems for a journal the same as with post-publication reviewers. Before a person is acknowledged, the author should send an exact copy of the acknowledgement and ask for written permission to acknowledge.

Copyright.—Authors and journal editors often are confused about *copyrights* and their legal aspects. The copyright laws of the United States are undergoing complete revision, but it is presumed that the general principles will remain the same. At the present time only a printed document, not a typescript or manuscript, can be copyrighted. Therefore copyrights are mainly the concern of the publisher, not the author. Secondly, certain kinds of information cannot be copyrighted; that is, their use in reprocessed form does not constitute an infringement. Examples of this are keys for identification, and descriptions of taxa. Only the format of such publications can be copyrighted. An infringement is involved only when the publication is reprinted in a manner that prevents or interferes with the sale of the original document. It follows that Data Documents cannot be copyrighted, and of course, there should be no need to do this with such material. Recent problems involve the use of xerography to produce portions of copyrighted documents for use in ways other than they are normally used by libraries and individuals. To make copies by xerography of copyrighted material does constitute an infringement. But it is not expected that the copyright holder will prosecute someone using these copies for ordinary purposes, i.e., cutting and filing. If, however, the copies prevent the sale of additional copies that might otherwise have been purchased, the copyright holder has reasonable cause to bring legal action against the infringer.

Authors should be concerned about one aspect of the present copyright law, however. It should be understood that if material is reproduced and distributed, as for example, class material distributed to students, it cannot later be copyrighted in book form. Therefore, authors should either secure a copyright on all such materials even in mimeographed or hectographed form, or instead, lend the copies to the students for the duration of the course and then call them back. The same holds true for governmental publications; they are public property and cannot be copyrighted. If the material is published in uncopyrighted form, it cannot later be copyrighted.

Author obligations to editors and publishers. – Once the document has been accepted, certain changes may be made, but only with the consent and understanding of the author. *Galley proof* is carefully *proof read*, marked using standard proof-readers marks (see Style Manual for Biological Journals, pp. 98-99, or an unabridged dictionary), and checked with the typescript. *Author's alterations* must be kept to a minimum. All changes made are billed as extra charges by the printer. The editor brings to the attention of the author any changes that are likely to be charged as author's alterations. The editor should realize that these can be very high if more than a few changes are made. Before the changes in matter already set in type are authorized by the editor, the author should indicate whether or not he is prepared to pay the extra cost. Other changes or additions not in the original typescript, for example, missing page numbers in a literature citation, or reference to previous pages by number, are marked as *queries* on the galleys. Authors must supply the missing data promptly.

Large works must be *indexed*. Indexing is usually done by the author. If he prefers, professional indexers are available, but the cost is charged to the author.

Journals usually make provision for supplying reprints to their authors, at the author's expense. This old tradition was once necessary, but modern copying equipment has made this an outmoded practice and journals would benefit if this needless procedure were discontinued. For many journals, it would mean an increased circulation. Many authors circulate reprints only to satisfy their vanity. The few copies that are really needed for official files and for those actually needing the article can be provided either as separates, tear copies, or photocopies. Other needs should be satisfied by the journal copies.

Some publication costs are passed on to the author. Usually he is expected to pay for the plate-making for illustrations and for the extra cost of setting the very expensive tabular matter. The recent years of inflation and abundant government grants have encouraged many journals to charge authors for part or all of the cost of publishing their articles. This has been encouraged by the granting agencies by permitting the inclusion of these fees in the budget of grant proposals. The SATCOM report presents a somewhat different view and tends to discourage the practice. It is obvious that if we are publishing too much unusable data and doing so in a very inefficient manner, page charges compound the error. This is discussed further in the following sections on publishing.

THE EDITOR

The editor of entomological periodicals and separate *works* is confronted with the same problems inherent in any other kind of publication. He must have the same training and the same experience as does a professional editor. Nearly always this is not the case. He is elected or appointed from the membership of the sponsoring society. Entomological publications, as with most biological publications, are written by amateurs, edited by amateurs, published by amateurs, and look like amateur work. The writing is frequently poor and the publication is put together without knowledge of printing design and without advance planning. Often the format is costly simply because neither the editor nor the publisher (the society) has any basic knowledge of printing.

The terminology needed by entomological publication editors is the same jargon as used by commercial publishers, but a glossary of their terms is not readily available to most entomological authors and many editors. The glossary included in this text contains a selection of terms chosen from a much longer list compiled during more than twenty years of editing by the author. Each printing term is used in the text, but without definition. These terms should be understood by those who have presumed to take on the appointment of editor, and many should be known by authors. Both groups might profit from a period of duty as a *printer's devil,* but in lieu of that, I recommend either a large endowment to the society for publication, or frequent consultation with a good printer. While the definitions of these terms in the glossary are meant to be accurate, they are not exhaustive, and in some cases I have taken certain liberties with the definitions to restrict the meaning for our own specialized needs.

Fortunately, the editors and authors of entomological publications now have a guide to follow, the *Style Manual for Biological Journals.* This book is poorly designed, showing the amateur status even of this, and should not be used as a format sample. For the most part, the text is sound. However, the amateur standing of this publication is further shown by the fact that its publisher makes no provision for sales to book stores so that the guide cannot be used as a class text without an extra mark-up to pass on to the irate student.

The "Style manual" is written and revised by the Council of Biology Editors, a group of editors of journals of biology and medicine of the United States concerned mainly with the establishment of a uniform format for journals. This uniform format is expected to make it easier for authors to prepare their papers and for editors to review and mark papers for printers. This project continues, but much needs to be done both in format design and in gaining universal acceptance of the format.

The first job of the editor as he begins the processing of documents is to continue the review of the typescript. Usually a publication has an editorial board. Often certain specialists are asked to examine the paper and give their opinions on the quality of the work. Once all of this information has been gathered, the editor must decide whether: 1) the paper is accepted for publication as is; 2) certain changes must be made before it will be accepted; 3) the paper is rejected. Forms or form letters are usually used for this. To save personal embarassment and to avoid lengthy argument over *rejected papers*, the form usually includes a variety of reasons for rejecting, but editors are not required to give specific explanations for this action. These decisions should be made as promptly as possible, usually within a month or at most two, and the authors notified accordingly.

Once a document has been accepted for publication, the skilled work of *editing* begins. Above all, the editor must keep to a publication schedule. He must prepare the *copy* for the printer. First, he must consider the arrangement of the paper; sometimes the sequence of parts need adjustment. Next, the hierarchy of subsections is examined for logic and consistency. This is followed by a careful examination of the contents, sometimes resulting in pruning excess verbiage, and in the elimination of duplication. If such changes are more than routine, *editorial liberties* must not be assumed in this kind of publishing, and the author's approval of the changes, as mentioned previously, should be secured in advance.

Marking the copy for *composition* by the printer involves a good knowledge of printing or the routine following of a preset pattern. Each of the subdivisions of the document must be marked for *type* size, *type face*, and *line measure*. All of this is a part of the format. The editor must be familiar with such terms as: *pica, point, italics, boldface, caps, small caps, lower case, font of type, spaces, leads,* and *foundry type*. Any errors made in marking copy are costly when changed. Changes when in galley are charged at high hourly rates and are time consuming because of the hand work necessary. Line drawings and halftones must be marked for size and the latter for *screen size*.

A printer usually takes about a month to set type and return the sets of galley proof. Three sets are needed: one for the author, one for changes to send to the printer, and one for marking for the make-up of the issue.

It is customary for authors to mark *corrections* and *deletions* with a *blue pencil* if these are corrections of printer's errors and with a red pencil if the changes are author's alterations to be charged to the author, or editorial changes to be charged to the journal. As mentioned previously, but cannot be over-emphasized, standard proof reader's marks should be used. It is surprising how many authors are not familiar with these marks. Illustrations much be checked for fidelity of reproduction. Halftone proof is submitted on coated paper for checking.

As soon as galley proof is returned by the authors to the editor, he must transfer all corrections to a set of the galleys to be returned to the printer. Then he is faced with the task of making-up the issue. If there are extensive corrections to be made, the editor may need a set of *revised proofs* before the page dummy can be made. The editor aims for *balanced pages* and an attractive issue. Type that will never be used (as for example, announcements that refer to an event already past) is marked as *killed type* on the galley and is later melted by the printer. Other type may be held as *overmatter* for a future issue, and some may be marked as *standing matter* (for example, the editorial policy and other cover information) to be used from issue to issue. Finally the table of contents is composed. This is best arranged by topics, these arranged alphabetically, but this is seldom done by biological editors. Usually articles are arranged by page order. This causes the user to read every title, a time consuming chore in publications like the *Journal* or *Annals* of the Entomological Society of America. Once all of these items have been checked, the material is returned to the printer.

The printer then prepares the issue and sends *page proof* to the editor. Page proof is sent to authors only if specifically requested because of extensive changes in the galley proof that need to be checked by the author. The proof is approved, and if an index is necessary, this may now be prepared. *Reprint* orders, if any, are compiled and sent to the printer along with the proofs and an order to print. Rarely revised page proofs are required. This completes the actual editing. The rest is up to the publisher.

THE PUBLISHER

The *publisher* is not to be confused with the *printer*. The latter actually produces the printed pages, but the former, who seldom has any printing equipment, is concerned with the design and marketing of the printed product. The publisher contracts with three agents, the editor and his staff, the purchaser or subscribers, and the printer.

Most entomological publications are produced by not-for-profit organizations. The scant publication of entomological information by for-profit concerns merely reflects the low volume demand for data on insects and their control; most of this kind of information is provided free either by the government or by societies.

As previously discussed, periodicals are abundant for entomology, with nearly all of them published by societies. The names of these publications are selected apparently without much consideration of the literal meaning of their descriptors. For example, we find the following as title terms: *annals, bulletin, contribution, gazette, journal, magazine, proceedings, review,* and *transactions*. Although it is too late to change these names for existing publications to give a true description of the type of contents of each, careful consideration of their meaning should be given before any new publication is named.

Societies producing the journals also may publish a monographic serial of unrelated topics. Most of them are rather poorly designed, scarcely advertized, costly to produce, and time consuming for all involved. It seems to me that more careful planning, especially with the help of some of the very fine university presses, would result in a better product, less costly of time and money. We generally think of books as the product of one person, but this is an inefficient way to compile and reprocess information. More and more textbooks and monographs are the product of a group of researchers under the direction of an efficient editor. Hopefully, this trend will continue, but danger lies in the committee type of product. If a committee produces a volume without the strong direction of a good editor, watered down statements and compromise organization will result. The SATCOM report is a good example of poor writing and a poor example of good organization because of committee actions and debates, paradoxical as this may be.

The publisher is concerned with five distinct phases of his art: obtaining typescripts from editors; editing (as discussed above); page and *volume* designing (format); producing the volume including the economics of production, and distributing the product to the consumer. Most entomological authors volunteer their product, giving it to the prospective publisher without recompense, often even assisting financially to produce it. This may partly account for the over-production of poorly processed data, but, of course, it is not that simple. Some very poor products are occassionally purchased by publishers. The economics of publishing is a complex matter beyond the scope of this text.

Format design of both page and volume is closely related to demand for the product, i.e., the money available. Obviously if each periodical and each book had a large circulation, considerable money could be spent on design and a very pleasing, artistic product could be produced. There are certain decisions that must be made regardless of the budget. The hope is that those involved will choose the most efficient alternative and then use the media to their best advantage to produce an artistic product.

The four main things to decide are method of printing; kind of *paper*; composition, including the selection of type faces, and kind of binding. These decisions are usually made by the *managing editor*, who also selects the printer.

Printing methods range from office type duplicators, through *offset* and *letterpress*. The latter two media need to be carefully considered. Many people mistakenly believe that there are great savings to be made by using offset printing. This may or may not be so. Much depends upon the type of composition selected, the number and kind of illustrations, and the number of copies to be printed.

The method of *composing* involves not only the wide variety of type faces available for *linotype* and *monotype,* but some of the very pleasing new methods of *typewriter composition* using *proportional spacing.* A *justified right hand margin* is possible, but not necessary in every case. This method of composition is suited to offset printing. Most letterpress printing is done either by linotype or monotype composition.

A very new method of production called Electronic Graphics (a Service Mark of R. R. Donnelley and Sons, Co.) is a means of high-speed typesetting using a character generator, the Videocomp, which is a combination of a computer and a cathode ray tube. By using computer files on magnetic tape, paper tape, or punched cards, the record may be converted to camera ready copy for offset reproduction by incorporating graphic arts instructions including the design of the type face. The Videocomp generates type at 1,000 to 4,000 characters a second. It scans as closely as 1,800 strokes per inch instead of the less than 100 per inch found in home television sets. As few as 50 or as many as 1,000 instructions may be required to create an individual character, but this is done in thousandths of a second.

Once the type of press work and the kind of composition is selected, the kind of paper can be chosen. Coated (glossy) paper is usually used because scientific publications frequently have a large number of half-tone illustrations. The size of the *page* should be decided upon only after consultation with the printer. Efficiency in paper use will depend upon the size of the press to be used, which in turn determines the *sheet* size and the number of pages in a *signature.* The signature size will also determine the number of pages in an issue. The number of signatures in an issue will dictate the type of *binding* used.

The esthetics of printing is related to the choice of type faces, the paper, the page size, the layout of the text on the page, illustrations, the use of *reverse plates,* and other devices to make each page a work of art. I feel strongly that publishers should be concerned about this as a part of their responsibility. Busy days should not be devoid of beauty—

in this case, the beauty of the art of printing. The publisher's *imprint* on the front of a volume should be matched by his pride in his *colophon* at the end.

The publisher of a society periodical is faced with the annoying problem of providing additional copies of an article to the author for his own private distribution. This archaic tradition has been discussed briefly above. If reprints are desired, these are ordered from the printer by the publisher. Reprints of articles with extraneous matter removed requires additional *make-ready*. The printer must charge for this. Until recently, the true cost of reprints was partly hidden in the total printing bill. Societies offering reprints at a low cost to authors were actually bearing most of this additional charge as a part of their printing bill. To keep from increasing printing charges to keep up with inflation, many printers have begun to pass on to the publisher the true cost of producing reprints. This has resulted in higher charges to authors, who in turn are finding that their sponsors are alarmed over these increased prices. Actually, entomological journals would do well to adopt the practice of many commercial publishers, that of letting the author arrange with an offset printer to produce reprints from clean copies of the journal. The journal publisher can easily supply two copies of the journal to each author for this purpose. Occasionally *separates* are provided instead, and these are distributed by some periodicals in advance of the bound issues. *Tear sheets* are by far the best means of satisfying the need for extra copies. The publisher supplies these from over-runs of the issue.

The distribution of an issue demands an entirely different set of skills. It is essentially a business procedure and should be handled by those familiar with these specialized activities. The *yearly subscription fee* should be accurately determined based on a business analysis, not on a ballot determination of what the members think they want. In order to set the fee, all costs must be determined, which includes the size and frequency of issue, mailing and other operating costs, and the potential number of paid subscribers. Packaging and mailing needs to be carefully considered. Some publications use a *second class mailing permit*, but may actually save money by using a bulk mailing permit or the *special fourth class rate*. Much depends upon the size of the mailing list, the frequency of mailing, and the amount of advertising. The special fourth class rate is extremely slow, however, and should be avoided for typescripts, proof, and dated materials. Even

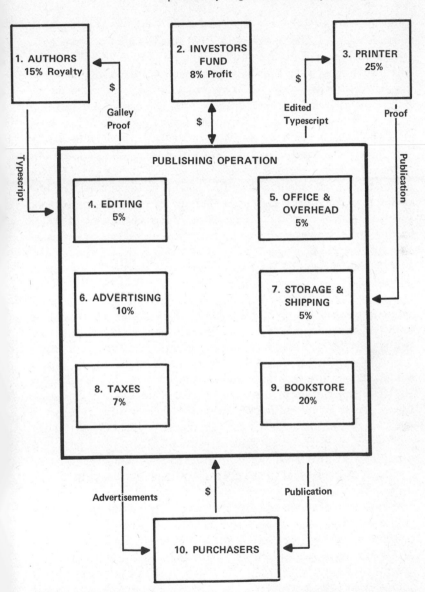

Fig. 7. Flowchart showing the process of publishing a book or journal. The percentages indicate the distribution of the list price of the book, or the annual subscription fee.

at second class rates delivery is very slow for publications with limited subscription lists. The matter of *zip code numbers* must be attended to by the publisher. These are now required on all types of bulk mailing. The proper form of an address and the choice of addressing machines require still further study. It is surprising how many persons do not know how to write a proper three or four line mailing address. For example, it is not necessary to spell out a state name. The two letter state abbreviations used by the Post Office Department with the zip code number, without a comma between the two, is adequate. The address should be designed to aid mail delivery, not to give all of the departments, sections, and subsections making up the internal structure of an organization. Finally, the keeping of subscription records, supplying missing numbers, and recording address changes are time consuming, unrewarding activities that must be done with absolute accuracy and efficiency.

A flowchart and PERT are extremely useful tools for the planning and the operation of any publishing activity. Such a chart is shown in figure 7. The percentages represent the proportion of time involved, or the portion of the publishing dollar. Part of this budgeting of a journal is currently included in the page charges to authors. Although this is permitted by granting agencies, as mentioned above, it is certainly to be discouraged, and every effort should be made to pay authors rather than charge them for the material they supply. If authors are paid, their product can be controlled, improved, and made useful. As it is now, authors feel that they have a right, provided by their membership in a society and by the fact that they pay for the publication, to publish their material without charge. Also note how much of this cost is saved by free editorial and publishing time donated by society members and their employers who permit this activity during working time!

The various boxes on the flowchart (figure 7) indicate an operation, each one of which is necessary and cannot be eliminated in some form or another, although each one is not always obvious in the production of a scholarly journal. You will note, taking each box in numerical order, that authors are due a 15% royalty, as shown in box number 1. Journal authors do not receive this. Book authors usually get a royalty payment approximating the 15% indicated here. Investors hope to receive 8% as profit, but journal publishers profit only by exchanging publications with others and in that way build their library. Box 3 shows 25% of the income going to the printer. Journal publishers will find this hard to accept unless they realize that the rest of their publishing operation is donated. These donated services are shown in boxes 4, 5, 6, 7, 8, and 9. When the purchaser, box 10, receives his publications, many hours of work have been spent to manufacture this product. Society members must begin to realize this, and accept higher charges in the future. Donated time is becoming scarcer. If members were required to pay the real cost of production, there would be many less periodicals and less raw data published.

Publication problems.—The SATCOM report gives five publication problems of concern to publishers at this time. These are essentially those that I have listed below, but my list pertains to the particular problems found in entomological publications. There is no simple

---

ENTOMOLOGICAL PUBLISHING PROBLEMS

Too many journals with a low number of subscribers resulting in a high per-page cost.

Provincial nature of both domestic and foreign publications and the consequent difficulty in their circulation outside of large or very specialized libraries.

The over-publication of unusable or once-read data more properly stored in archives as is other historical documentation.

The great time lag between the completion of a project and the availability of the published information.

The lack of coordination of publications by editors so as to prevent overlapping publication of some kinds of data.

---

solution to the publication problem. I will close this chapter, therefore, by listing a few suggestions of things that might be done to improve the situation, but I will leave their promulgation to those active during the new decade.

PUBLICATION IMPROVEMENT IN ENTOMOLOGY

Reduce the number of journals.

Improve the quality and lag time (SATCOM recommendations C9, C10).

Standardize coding and indexing of papers (SATCOM recommendation C4) with author required abstracts and indexes (descriptors) (SATCOM recommendation C3).

Establish SDI centers.

International cooperation among abstracting and indexing services (SATCOM recommendation C2).

Establish review journals (SATCOM recommendation C10).

Facilitate international circulation of publications including centralized depots and reprocessing centers.

Economic improvement of journals by production of useful publications resulting in improved circulation and commercial support (see SATCOM recommendations C7, C8, and C13).

Reduce the number of "preliminary" papers by providing other means for publication (e.g., SDI) and clarifying editorial policies so that the medium will not be used as a means of producing "required" reports to contracting and granting agencies (see SATCOM recommendation C16).

ASSIGNMENT 4

4.1 Study the editorial policy of the Annals or Journal of the Entomological Society of America. Then prepare an outline and format for a paper you might write on a subject of your choice.

4.2 Obtain a practice galley proof and make all of the necessary corrections using proof reader's marks.

OPTIONAL INVESTIGATION

Write the above outlined paper and submit it for editing.

REVIEW CHECKLIST

1. Using the glossary, define the printing and publishing terms printed in italics in this chapter.
2. Who are the principle persons involved in publishing?
3. What particular qualities should an author keep in mind as he composes his product?
4. Explain briefly the duties of the editor. The publisher.
5. Name the major steps in the dissemination of information as outlined on the chart, figure 6.

6. Name at least three main reasons why a scientific paper is published.
7. What are the three elements of a title?
8. Name two important features of an abstract.
9. What are the features of typescript preparation that should receive special attention?
10. Discuss briefly factors to be considered in preparing illustrations for publication.
11. What are the reasons for prepublication reviews by the sponsoring institution? By the publisher?
12. What is a copyright? How is it secured? How is it used?
13. Discuss editor-author relationships; publisher-author relationships.
14. What are the production problems of reprints?
15. What publication costs are passed on to the authors? Discuss their validity.
16. What special skills are needed by an editor?
17. What three agents are dealt with by the publisher? Relate this to the publishing flowchart, figure 7.
18. What is meant by the art of printing?
19. Discuss briefly some of the production methods possible as the media of the art of printing.
20. What are the particular publishing problems for entomology?
21. Discuss some possible solutions.

CHAPTER 6

PREPARATION OF DOCUMENTS FOR INFORMATION
RETRIEVAL

We are already aware that the most critical aspect of IRS is the *indexing* or coding of documents. As discussed previously, the association or organization of data permits the formation of a hypothesis. The coding of the data is the statement of this hypothesis because the *code terms* selected shows the association of ideas. This is exactly the process followed when a new taxon is described and named. It is the procedure followed when a phenomenon is investigated. The terms used in each case reflect the concepts.

In the IRS the coding process is necessary both for the storing of information and for its retrieval. Requests must be coded to match the code terms used when a document was placed in the information bank. Coding is, therefore, exactly the same as making an identification, or a diagnosis. It is a means of tagging a phenomenon. To name something is to make an identification and does no more than relate phenomena. This is achieved when the code and the search request are matched. The importance of this in all aspects of life was predicted by Sabrosky in 1967: "When men land on the moon, they will collect samples.

Then they will ask the elementary question in taxonomy: "What is it?" And then they will submit it for identification to some taxonomist!" We have refined and perfected this information coding system through the cooperative efforts of taxonomists and all others in the field of entomology.

WHAT CAN BE CODED

All coding is reduced to words or numbers that are abbreviations for words. Words, therefore, are codes or symbols for concepts, and because words are composed of letters, each of which is a symbol by itself, it has been a simple matter to translate these into the computer language. Abortive attempts have been made to devise an international language. Esperanto, for example, has not been widely received for many reasons, the most important of which is the fact that it solves no communication problem any better than an existing language. It merely adds one more language to be learned. Recently a trend toward the use of simple designs to label a place, an apparatus, or a situation has become evident. For example, in bilingual countries in particular, traffic control signs in two languages are replaced by a design that serves as a symbol of a concept. This can be recognized instantly without reading and translating, certainly an advantage both in traffic control when reaction speed is essential and in other aspects of modern rapid pace living. Even automobiles of foreign makes have their controls labelled with picturegraphs to indicate the use of the levers. We may expect increasing employment of symbol language, and eventually this may even replace a major portion of printed language. If so, we can expect more rapid learning with no loss of concept in translation through variations in context.

Pictures, sounds, and machine tracings can be coded also, but as explained previously, seldom is more done than to give these documents a title as a caption. Application of the same coding procedure as for printed documents to these is encouraged. Some features necessary for coding photographs and drawings are discussed later in this chapter.

Our main concern here is to outline procedures for coding printed documents including those dealing with insect taxonomy. The International Code of Zoological Nomenclature provides us with a good set of rules under which zoological names are formulated and used. The name of the organism is a means of indicating the existence of a species, and therefore, a biological phenomenon. The system of nomenclature used by taxonomists is not only a coding system, but serves as a way to sort names into groups. These groups then become a means of information retrieval.

REVIEW OF THE TYPES OF INFORMATION CODES

We are already familiar with several types of codes. A review of these will illustrate the principles involved, which may then be applied to all other types of information coding.

The title of a document, when properly constructed, is the shortest possible description of the contents of the document. It is easy to observe that titles vary greatly in length. Sometimes it is possible to use a single word as a title, for example, "insects". One would expect to find general information about all groups of insects in this publication. "A field guide to the insects", as a title, further restricts the scope of the publication. The only code word available for the first title is INSECTS, but for the second, INSECTS and FIELD GUIDE are code words that, in combination, restrict the indication of the contents of the publication. Thus, to search for all of the literature on insects and all of the field guides to organisms would be an extremely large job. But to search for all of the insect field guides would be a task that could be relatively easily accomplished. The A, TO, and THE in the title are only supportive words that contribute nothing to the concept of the contents of the document. These can be left out entirely without any change in meaning. The addition of the words NORTH AMERICA to the title would be further restrictive action. A search for a document meeting these characteristics would be simple indeed.

From this account one can see that the title 1) should be a restrictive coding of contents, and 2) provide only a limited analysis of the subject content of the document. For further analysis, other parts of the document must be studied.

Many documents have as an accessory to the text, the abstract. This may be a part of the document, or a separate document published in an abstract journal, or it may be published both with the document and separately. The preparation and use of abstracts and abstract search resources are considered in chapter 8. Abstracts usually provide all words necessary for a set of descriptors and, therefore, provide a source for code terms. However, they may not contain all of the names of the organisms included in the complete document.

A variation of the abstract often useful in current awareness publications is the *annotation,* a very short abstract containing additional restrictive words not found in the title. An example of an annotation follows the title of a book:

Lutz, Frank E., 1948. *Field Book of Insects,* G. P. Putnam's Sons, N. Y. 510 pp., 100 figs.

A manual for the identification of the insects of the United States and Canada.

This additional phrase offers these restrictive code terms: manual; identification; United States; Canada. With this additional source of available code words, we are able to determine more precisely the audience for the book. Often the annotation is sufficient for the complete coding of a document.

Class numbers, when the number or number-letter combination represent the document content, are forms of information codes. Universal class numbers are used in libraries for classifying, sorting, and locating books. The two systems used in the United States and Canada are the Library of Congress (using both letters and numbers) and the Dewey Decimal (using only numbers for the main classification) systems. Additional systems of class numbers are under consideration for the use with computer retrieval and some are discussed below.

The search for code terms next extends to the table of contents showing chapters and subheadings within the chapters. Assuming the book is properly written and that the editor understood the organization of the material, all necessary code terms will be found here. With this use in mind editors are urged to pay close attention to those features.

The final anatomical feature of a document used as a standard code term source is the index. A carefully prepared index will contain every code term for the information stored in the publication. However, the index must include a conceptual analysis, not just the terms used in the text. Words appear in the index because it refers to a code term, which, in turn, represents contributed information. Therefore, the index to any document serves as a retrieval mechanism. The conceptual analysis is necessary to make certain that all topics discussed in the text are indexed under all possible look-up or request code terms.

Unfortunately, not all publications are well indexed. Several of the desirable features listed below may be missing. A deficient index is

---

CHARACTERISTICS OF A GOOD INDEX

Complete list of terms used

Cross-indexing for conceptual analysis

Page numbers for each entry even if used as a cross-reference
(e.g., Coleoptera, see beetle, p. 5)

Author references indexed
(e.g., cited publication referred to by author's name and page
number on which the reference appears in the text)

All taxa listed

---

usually the result of the indexer's lack of a conceptual awareness of the subject. An index should be prepared either by the authors or in close collaboration with the authors.

So far this discussion has pointed out coding aids to be found primarily in books. Journal articles seldom provide code terms other than those in the title. Some of the better edited articles will have meaningful subheadings. A few journals have attempted to add code terms, as descriptors, to the article, but this has been inadequate so far because of the lack of a well prepared thesaurus (discussed later) and rules for coding.

The reader should now be able to relate the tab or index card of files and separation sheets of notebooks to the principles of coding. For a successful and useful card and notebook system, all of the features of books and related systems are necessary.

With the above in mind, the next step is, of course, to see the relationship of the holes in the key sort cards to coding. As expected, once the principles of coding are applied to any of these storage and retrieval systems, it will function. Although key sort cards have a specialized application, coding and retrieval principles are the same as for punch cards in an IRS.

ASSIGNMENT 5

5.1 Review each of the coding systems mentioned above and locate examples of these in the citation file you have already constructed. Test this coding system against an actual search request as a means of appraising the efficiency of the system. List any noted deficiencies and make suggestions for improvement.

5.2 Examine either the Library of Congress or Dewey Decimal system of book cataloging and be able to explain each part of the class number.

INFORMATION CODING PROCEDURE AND INDEX LANGUAGE

The *information coding* of documents follows few rules and generally permits less than 100% retrieval. Two important factors are responsible for this situation. First, the code terms, and the conceptual analysis of the document are made by an individual, so his emphasis and his interpretation of the work is reflected in his analysis. Second, only by a complete reading of the document is it ever possible to obtain all of the information contained in the document, and even this is only theoretically possible. Coding procedure is designed to approach 100% retrieval, only if practical. For example, an article describing a geological survey of a wild region might mention that certain insects were collected. Because this information is very incidental to the main purpose of the article, the only code term used in the analysis of the document might be "insects". In this case someone searching for information on a particular group of insects might well pass over this very general descriptor and the information on these insects would not be retrieved. To provide for 100% retrieval in this case would not be practical.

The procedure for coding varies from a search only of the title for key words, an analysis of the abstract, or a selection of words from the text, to a complete quanitative analysis of each term used in the document. For example, in the latter case, the number of times a particular term is used in the document will influence the selection of code words when the entire article is analyzed. The aim of the coding procedure is to construct a *document profile* of sufficient accuracy and depth as to assure that eventually, through the matching of a search *request profile*, closely related documents will be selected and irrelevant ones eliminated. As will be shown later, the thesaurus forms the connector that makes this a practical procedure.

Two distinct steps are involved in the information coding process. The indexer must have an *index language,* a complete set of terms used for indexing or coding to describe document content including the rules for their use, subheadings, and the order of reference for compound terms. This set of terms is the index vocabulary which is built up as documents are indexed and coded. The code terms are those that are selected from the index to describe the document.

The coder must judge from the title, abstract, subheadings, and if necessary, the contents of the document, the subjects or scope of the work. He should keep in mind the needs of the readers as well as the author's own statements. This analysis is for the purpose of making a useful document profile. This profile must be made within the context of the retrieval system used and the objectives of the service, i.e., the search request profile. The index language is used as the source of the code terms so far as terms are available.

In addition to the index, a *controlled vocabulary* is used as a list of subject class labels to be used in arranging or grouping documents. A vocabulary is always available to entomologists if they adopt the section classification (with some adjustment for this purpose) used by the Entomological Society of America. The following list of topics is a suggested vocabulary based on these sections. The code terms used in coding for the EDP retrieval system described in chapter 7 are given in brackets. These code terms are formed by four simple rules.

◻ Use the first eight letters whenever possible

◻ Use the first four letters of the first and last word when two or more words are used to form the index term.

◻ Use "y" for "ology" when that suffix cannot be spelled out.

◻ If by using these rules two code terms become identical, drop a vowel from the second term and add the next letter.

1. Biosystematics [BIOSYSTE]
   1.1 Taxonomy [TAXONOMY]
      1.100 Numerical [NUMERICA]
      1.200 Classification [CLASSIFI]
   1.2 Ecology [ECOLOGY*]

---

*The presence of the asterisk indicates a space to extend the word to eight characters.

1.3 Bionomics [BIONOMIC]
1.4 Behavior-[BEHAVIOR]
1.5 Genetics [GENETICS]
1.6 Morphology [MORPHOLY]
1.7 Comparative anatomy
[COMPANAT]
1.8 Phylogeny [PHYLOGEN]
1.9 Evolution [EVOLUTIO]
1.10 Speciation [SPECIATI]
1.11 Paleoentomology
[PALEOENY]
1.12 Zoogeography
[ZOOGEOGY]
1.13 Nomenclature
[NOMENACL]
1.14 Development
[DEVELOPM]
1.15 Metamorphosis
[METAMOR]
1.16 Faunistics [FAUNISTI]
2. Physiology [PHYSIOLY]
2.1 Cytology [CYTOLOGY]
2.2 Ultrastructure
[ULTRASTR]
2.3 Histology [HISTOLOY]
2.4 Organ systems
[ORGASYST]
2.5 System regulation
[SYSTREGU]
2.6 Genetics [GENETICS]
2.7 Functional anatomy
[FUNCANAT]
2.8 Effective environment
[EFFEENVI]
2.9 Insecticides [INSECTIC]
2.91 Metabolism
[METABOLI]
2.92 Resistance
[RESISTAN]

2.93 Chemistry
[CHEMISTR]
2.10 Biochemistry
[BIOCHEMI]
2.11 Toxicology
[TOXICOLY]
3. Ecology [ECOLOGY*]
3.1 Autecology
[AUTECOLY]
3.2 Population ecology
[POPUECOY]
3.3 Behavior
[BEHAVIOR]
3.4 Dispersal
[DISPERSA]
3.5 Host relationship
[HOSTRELA]
3.6 Social organization
[SOCIORGA]
3.7 Microbiology
[MICROBIY]
3.8 Pathology
[PATHOLOY]
3.9 Symbiosis
[SYMBIOSI]
3.10 Vectors
[VECTORS*]
3.11 Parasites
[PARASITE]
3.12 Husbandry
[HUSBANDR]
3.13 Biological Control
[BIOLCONT]
3.14 Bionomics
[BIONOMIC]
4. Medical and Veterinary
[MEDIVETE]
4.1 Protection
[PROTECTI]

4.2 Ectoparasites
[ECTOPARA]
4.3 Intermediate hosts
[INTEHOST]
4.4 Epidemics and epizootics
[EPIDEPIZ]
4.5 Household Insects
[HOUSINSE]
5. Extension and Regulatory
[EXTEREGU]
5.1 Area eradication
[AREAERAD]
5.2 Control program
[CONTPROG]
5.3 Quarantines
[QUARANTI]
5.4 Population surveys
[POPUSURV]
5.5 Detection
[DETECTIO]
5.6 Extension methods and
publicity
[EXTEPUBL]
5.7 Legal aspects
[LEGAASPE]
6. Crop protection
[CROPPROT]
6.1 Control of crop pests
[CONTPEST]
6.2 Forest entomology
[FOREENTO]

6.3 Control technique
[CONTTECH]
6.4 Crop production loss
[CROPLOSS]
6.5 Pesticides
[PESTICID]
6.51 Residues
[RESIDUES]
6.52 Public health
[PUBLHEAL]
6.53 Wildlife
[WILDLIFE]
7. Technique
[TECHNIQU]
7.1 Literature
[LITERATU]
7.2 Experimentation
[EXPERIME]
7.3 Field work
[FIELWORK]
7.4 Specimens and collec-
tions
[SPECCOLL]
7.5 Biometry
[BIOMETRY]
7.6 Data storage and re-
trieval
[DATARETR]
8. Popular literature
[POPULITE]
9. History [HISTORY*]

Many topics are omitted in the preceding list, or, they are not arranged in a manner for conceptual analysis. To supplement this list, the terms and their arrangement as used in *Zoological Record* can be used. Because this publication treats the literature of the world, use of this publication as an index tool is a logical step toward a unified list of thesaurus words. The terms as they are given on the following pages is in the same order as they appear in this publication.

It is hoped that this might be used by any developing IRS as the basis for their thesaurus. By doing this, they will automatically tie into this over 100 year old index and provide a means for easy retrospective search.

General
  Textbooks, treatises
  Historical
  Biography
  Bibliography
  Taxonomy
  Nomenclature
  Collections
  Technique
    Collecting and preserving
    Breeding and experimental
    Anatomical
    Illustration
    Miscellaneous
Morphology
  General anatomy
  Biometrics
  Exoskeleton, integument
  Color
  Scales and hairs
  Head
  Eyes
  Antennae
  Mouthparts
  Thorax
  Wings
  Legs
  Abdomen
  Alimentary system
  Respiratory system
  Circulatory system
  Excretory system
  Reproductive system
  Genital armature

Nervous system
Sense organs
Sound-producing organs
Light-producing organs
Myology
Fat body
Glands
Scent organs
Histology, cytology
Early stages
Pupae
Larvae and nymphs
Eggs
Teratology
Development
  General
  Sexual maturation
  Spermatogenesis
  Oogenesis
  Embryology
  Cytology
  Tissues and organs
  Metamorphosis
  Moulting
  Diapause
  Growth
  Effects of temperature and humidity
  Effects of irradiation
  Effects of food
  Effects of various factors
  Sex ratio
  Sex determination
  Gynandromorphs, intersexes

Hybrids
Parthenogenesis
Regeneration, transplantation
Physiology
Body temperature
Integument
Vitality and longevity
Digestion and nutrition
Respiration
Haemolymph, circulation
Excretion
Secretion, external
    internal
Reproduction
Fecundity
Nervous system
Senses
Movements, attitudes
Tropisms
Rhythm
Sound production
Effects of temperature and
    humidity
Effects of various factors
Effects of mutilation
Chemistry, analytical
    metabolic
Water balance
Luminosity
Coloration
Miscellaneous
Bionomics
General habits, life histories
Insects
Movements, attitudes
Flights
Sex relations
Oviposition
Parental care

Nests
Larval cases; cocoons
Social and gregarious insects
Bee life
Wasp life
Ants and myrmecophiles
Termites and termitophiles
Ecology
General problems
Insects and weather
Phenology, generations
Hibernation, aestivation
Feeding habits, phytophagous
Leaf-miners
Galls
Insects and flowers
Feeding habits, predacious
    Miscellaneous
Symbosis
Internal symbionts
Entomolophagous parasites
Parasites of other animals
Disease carriers
Insect diseases
Insectivorous plants
Predacious animals
Dispersal, migration
Population studies
Land insects
Soil insects
Aquatic insects
Cave insects
Miscellaneous
Evolution
General problems
Phylogeny
Genetics
Variation
Dimorphism, polymorphism

Coloration
Mimicry
Melanism
Geography or faunistic (incl.
    fossil faunas)
Zoogeography
The World
Arctic, Antarctic
Insular, incl. New Zealand
Palearctic Region
Europe, collectively
North Europe and Siberia
British Isles
France
Central and Eastern Europe
South Europe
Mediterranean Islands
North Africa

Africa
Madagascar and Mascarene
Caucasus, West and Central
    Asia
    Islands
Asia, Tropical and Eastern
Asiatic Archipelago
Indo-Australian Region
    collectively
Papuan Sub-region
Australia
America, collectively
North America
Central America
South America, incl. Trinidad
Antilles
Fossil faunas

Each of the code terms given in these lists may be arranged alphabetically and used with the retrieval system proposed in chapter 7. Note that the same system can be used for names of organisms so that retrieval may be made using any desired taxon. In all cases the eight letter code term must be devised. However, each term used must be derived so that each remains unique. The building of this kind of vocabulary will take study and cooperation on a national and international basis if the hoped-for network of EDP information retrieval systems are to become a reality.

BIOSIS has established a set of index terms for the CROSS index they produce. It is for internal use and has as a controlled vocabulary 85 major headings and over 500 subheadings for all branches of biology. The average number of subject headings to which an abstract is assigned is six.

After the document has been analyzed for the subject content, a *conceptual analysis* must be made. This is, as we have seen, the making of an identification. The subjects are matched with a *classification schedule* which is a listing of index or subject headings arranged in a generic and specific classification to bring like terms together. For example, a book is analyzed by a librarian using a standard classification schedule such as the Dewey Decimal system. The result of this analysis is a *notation,* or a code listing for the classification schedule as a short-hand reference. These are referred to as class numbers and are obtained from the classification schedule. The same procedure must be used for each document processed. The care in which this is done determines the efficiency of the retrieval.

We have referred many times to the thesaurus, the term often used by those interested in establishing an index language for coding. This dictionary or index of synonyms and antonyms is useful in making the conceptual analysis for the reasons that it will list terms in their various contexts so that the analizer may determine the way to list the contents of a document in the subject index no matter how ideas may vary from analyzer to analyzer. The thesauri are constructed only after continued use, and must be continually studied and refined as the work on the IRS progresses.

A THESAURUS OF TERMS SHOULD CONTAIN

An indication of synonyms showing the accepted and deprecated terms

A display of terms in alphabetical sequence

An arrangement of terms within groups or categories permitting access to specific terms leading from the more general concept

Evidence of generic-specific relationships (broader and narrower terms)

Indication of suggested related terms frequently associated with an individual term

---

The final indexing of the document now involves the translation of the document profile into the *index terms* to be used in the retrieval system, no matter what kind of system is used. The indexing, using the code terms (=the index terms to be used as the final notation for the document) must be arranged into a hierarcy of words. This arrangement must agree with the *subject index* showing this arrangement. These *subject headings* are used as they appear in the controlled vocabulary.

As soon as these three steps have been completed, the document is stored in the information bank. The document code profiles are then made available for matching with the search request profiles in the IRS.

Various systems of *machine indexing* or coding are under study and a few are in operation (see SATCOM recommendation E4). The most widely used system at the present time is B.A.S.I.C. of the Bioscience Information Service, Inc. (BIOSIS). This involves the *permutation of terms* given in the title by means of a computer program. The details of this are discussed further in chapter 8. In essence, the title of the document provides the code words, and through a computer program, enriched titles are arranged so that each index word appears in an alphabetical listing of the titles, the title repeated for each key word. Because the title is enriched it serves as a *key word out of context (KWOC)* system. If the title were not enriched it would be necessary to have words related to each other for retrieval; this would be a *key word in context (KWIC)* system. Many other similar systems have been proposed. The deficiency of the system is the inherent lack of adequate titles. Enrichment by the editors of B.A.S.I.C. by the addition of some necessary code terms as a part of the title before permutation permits a greater percentage of retrieval.

Until computer scanning has been perfected for information retrieval, complete machine indexing will remain a dream for the future. Once it is practical to machine read a document, an EDP-IRS will become a simple procedure for scientific literature.

___

ASSIGNMENT 5 (Cont.)

5.3 Review each of the citation cards you have prepared so far for this series of assignments, and code the documents according to the principles outlined above. Remember that eight characters for each code term will be used in the assignments to follow.

5.4 Construct a thesaurus for your future use. It is suggested that you correlate yours with any other that may be available to you.

___

UP-DATING OF CODING

We have emphasized several times previously in this discussion the need for a uniform system of coding, and a set of rules to follow as coding proceeds. Neither of these requirements has been met at the present time. We are now at the same stage in information retrieval as the taxonomist was before there was a code of nomenclature. It seems apparent that concentrated effort should be made for the establishment of the "International Rules of Biological Information Coding."

The need to up-date the coding of documents will be apparent only when a retrospective search is required. Naturally documents that have not been completely coded cannot be retrieved until necessary code terms are supplied. Although it is not generally apparent, it may help to include "negative" code terms to show that certain kinds of information are NOT present even if the citation may lead one to believe that the information is in the document.

Up-dating is possible only if the system of code terms for each document includes a unique bibliographic citation or a unique document profile. If such a combination of terms is devised, it would be possible then to add further code terms either to the citation or the profile. Otherwise it is necessary to return to the document storage file and recode to up-date. Which of the three systems are used will depend upon several factors, particularly the structuring of the IRS and the method of tie-in with other systems. If carefully planned in the beginning, it is possible for any independently developed system to tie-in with any other without a strictly uniform thesaurus. It follows then that any system can be up-dated in the same way, and retrospective searches would be possible as older citations are added (see SATCOM recommendation E6).

INDEXING PHOTOGRAPHS AND DRAWINGS

No general system for indexing photographs and drawings other than by reference to their captions appear to be available. Captions are written for a specific purpose, i.e., to illustrate a point in the text. Therefore, they may not contain all of the index words necessary for a complete description of the features of these records. I am aware of only one attempt to index illustrations, i.e., to place in the index the words contained in the caption of the illustrations. Unfortunately, this could not be done thoroughly because the captions were written and set into type before the system described below was devised.

Three main features may be found in most illustrations: 1) the place, if a photograph of a region, or the type of illustration, i.e., diagram, photomicrograph, drawing, or other appropriate term; 2) subject, as a part of an organism, stage, orientation (i.e., dorsal view, cross-section, etc.), and magnification; 3) name of taxa or phenomena illustrated.

Care should be taken in caption writing to see that each of these three features are included or otherwise accounted for. The order in which they are used will depend upon the purpose of the illustration. The first sentence of the caption should contain all three elements with following ,entences giving further details if needed. With these features described, it is easier to determine the code terms to use for the retrieval of information that might be lost otherwise.

TREATMENT OF SPECIMENS IN AN IRS

The processing of the information documents and the flow of information through the system requires the same treatment regardless of the kind of records used. Taxonomists process their information by identifying specimens. They use as the point of reference the holotype specimen or its substitute. Through this name association, the documents dealing with organisms are stored and retrieved. Therefore, the information that is generated by specimens is stored and retrieved only through the code terms which we call the scientific name.

Once a specimen has been accurately identified, thus providing a name, the most important step in the preparation of information storage has been completed. Accurate means should be devised to positively associate individual specimens with information because if identification errors are made the concept of the species involved may change. If data and specimens cannot be associated individually, the data may be useless. The need for a standardized format for this information association has become acute. As the volume of data mounts, a higher percentage of it becomes inaccessible.

The system returns information documents only by the correct use of the name as the index. The information retrieved describes the variation, distribution, and biological knowledge about the species. Several uses of retrieved information have been pointed out previously (Arnett, 1967a). These are repeated here with the hope of encouraging a more general awareness of the need for this kind of information.

Holotypes and topotypic populations. — A single specimen does not provide enough information for scientific treatment. Holotype specimens are no exception and it has never been claimed that they served anything other than nomenclatural purposes. This being so, there seems to be no valid scientific reason for continuing to treasure poor holotypes, and there is no practical reason why neotypes should be restricted to replacing lost or destroyed holotypes, while retaining useless originals. As the taxonomist attempts to associate data with names, he may find a hopeless impass because the holotype does not provide the needed data.

Accepting the premise that the scientific method requires repeatability, it follows that specimens of extant species should be recoverable from the field. One way to demonstrate this is to match holotypes with specimens from the field. If, for example, a holotype lacks specific locality information, but can be matched with specimens from a restricted locality, that is, it agrees almost exactly with another variant so that there is little doubt that the extant deme represents a breeding population containing the same variants as the holotype, that population may be regarded as topotypic regardless of whether it is now at the same locality as it was when the holotype specimen was collected. Specimens studied from that population may then supply biological information attributable to the holotype. With these as the anchor for the name, it is a simple matter to continue studies on related populations to help understand the variation and perhaps even the speciation of the group.

Further studies of the area surrounding the restricted 'topotypic" population and the gathering of information about these areas may serve to circumscribe a breeding population. It follows that by so doing, other such populations may be circumscribed, making possible the study of isolates if such exist. The holotype then serves as the link between biological data and the information storage and retrieval system.

INTERNATIONAL CODE OF ZOOLOGICAL NOMENCLATURE

Before an organism can be discussed in the literature, it must be named. Much of the work in entomology is the processing of these names because they are the code terms used to open the door to all of previous information on the taxa. Without a uniform name it would be very inconvenient to try to refer to a particular species. The names are applied to species and to groups of species. A sincere attempt is made to prevent duplication of names so that there is one name for one species.

". . . for whatsoever Adam called any living creature the same is its name.' —Genesis, 2: 19. This often quoted passage indicates the arbritrary nature of the naming process itself, but has no reference to the validity of the group named. In dealing with nomenclature, we are concerned with literature only, not with the organisms themselves.

In order to have a single name for a single species, definite rules have been proposed for the universal naming of organisms. These highly technical rules are termed the "International Rules of Zoological Nomenclature" for zoologists, and there are several other similar sets of rules for other groups of organisms. All of these rules have the same major features. Entomologists have adopted the rules that apply to animals and follow these rules by common consent. This has had a considerable effect on the entomological literature as we have already shown by repeated reference to the "Code". The general use of these rules makes necessary not only an understanding of their provisions by all taxonomists but also all entomologists should have some knowledge of how they are used. This will enable the proper use of names as a means for information retrieval.

THE PROVISIONS OF THE CODE INCLUDE

The naming of taxa
The law of priority
The type species of a genus
Homonyms
Synonyms
Type specimens

The crux of taxonomy is the name of the organisms, for with it, whether accurately or inaccurately determined, one stores, associates, and retrieves information and it is, therefore, a coding system. The name serves as the turnstile, and often the bottleneck, of information flow. Taxonomists long ago devised this, their own rigid system for uniformity in storing information for easy retrieval, the binominal system. The storage procedure is to a great extent controlled by this now generally accepted Code. The ONLY bridge between the system and biological data is the type specimen, the holotype, the lectotype, or the neotype.

Much confusion in the presentation of taxonomic data is due to the failure to conceive of the Code as the means of programming the storage and retrieval of biological information about organisms. The program requires only name data to operate, but too frequently the input lacks accurate and detailed information associated with names and specimens, and fails to associate biological information with names correctly associated with types. The method of treating names is described in this section as a part of the coding process.

Dating of publications.—As shown by H. S. Barber and J. C. Bridwell (1940) and many others, the dates printed on a publication are not always the *date of publication.* For example, the so-called "Dejean Catalog" was issued in parts over a period of years, and in several editions. Only after careful research involving the history of this book as published in society proceedings of the time, and a study of the type used to print the various editions, were these authors able to date the contents. The dating of the new generic names included in the volumes hinge on this research. In only a very few cases has any of this research involved an important name change. Blackwelder (1967) has discussed this in detail and cited several examples. As long as the law of priority is an important part of the name stabilizing procedure, the exact dating of publications is necessary.

Abbreviated rules of nomenclature.—The Code governs the way descriptions are treated, the assembling of catalogs, and the correct name to be applied to an animal. This, in turn, determines to a large extent the value of much of the available entomological literature. For example, the literature published prior to 1758 has only historical value, as does much of the literature for the following 100 years. Yet the latter must be accounted for when animals are properly named. This creates a rather unusual situation in science, and one that will require much time to survey. Details of the Code are beyond the scope of this book and are very well treated in Blackwelder (1967). The following abbreviated rules may be used to understand the principles needed to complete the assignments that follow.

The main provisions of the Code are:

1. The object of the rules is to provide a system under which the name of each taxon (taxonomic group) is unique and distinct in the "animal kingdom."

2. Two names are used for species-groups, i.e., a species must belong to a genus, and the species-group name is composed of the generic name and the specific name.

3. The scientific name of an animal must be a word that is either Latin or Latinized from the Greek, or a proper name Latinized.

4. Orders and higher taxonomic categories are to be used in accord-

ance with an established list, and new names for these higher categories are not to duplicate those already in use.

5. Family-group names are to have the termination "idae" for family, and "inae" for subfamily. Both names are to be based on a type genus selected from the genera included in the family or subfamily.

6. Genus-group names must be treated as nouns; they always must be capitalized.

7. Species-group names may be adjectives, nouns in apposition, possessive nouns, participles, or gerunds. All are treated as adjectives, and placed in grammerical agreement with any generic-group name with which it may be combined; they always must be written with a small initial letter.

8. The author of a name is that person who first published the name, and his name follows immediately behind the name of the organism described; where the date of publication is cited, the name and date are to be separated by a comma; when a specific name has been removed to a genus other than the one in which it was originally described, the author's name, and date, if cited, are placed in parentheses.

9. New names are validly published only when printed by some mechanical process that insures (reasonably) duplication on apparently durable paper, with "ink", and that each copy is an exact duplicate, these copies must be offered for sale and be distributed (microfilming does not constitute publication, but xeroxed print-outs of microfilm does; mimeograph and similar duplication is discouraged).

10. The 10th edition of the *Systema Naturae* of Linnaeus (1758) is the work that is accepted as the starting point of zoological nomenclature, and of the law of priority. All other works published in 1758 are treated as having been published after this work.

11. The law of priority provides that the first published available name is to be used, and that consequently, the oldest available name is retained when any part of an animal, any stage, sex, or any generation is named, provided these names fulfill the requirement specified in the Code.

12. Genera are to have a type species designated by selection and indicated as "type species of the genus", no longer as "genotype."

13. Type specimens are selected either as a holotype, a specimen selected and designated at the time of original description, a lectotype, a specimen later selected from the original series, or a neotype, a single specimen designated by a later author when the type or type series is known to be destroyed.

14. A generic name is to be rejected as a homonym when it has been used previously for some other genus of animals or a previous emendation of another name has been made, making the spelling identical with another genus, but it is not a homonym if there is a spelling difference of even one letter; diacritic marks are not to be used, but such letters are to be spelled out.

15. A specific name is to be rejected when it is discovered that an older, identical, validly proposed name exists in the same genus (junior primary homonym) only while the condition of homonymy is considered still to exist.

16. Differences in spelling are to be disregarded in determining specific homonymy if the specific names are in fact the same word.

17. One who observes that a name is an invalid homonym should, if possible, so notify the author, and should then allow him an opportunity to publish a substitute name.

18. The interpretation of the Rules is referred to and acted upon by a permanent body, the International Commission on Zoological Nomenclature.

The current Code became in effect November 6, 1961, and the changes in the 1964 edition became in effect May [1], 1964.

In order to use our system of nomenclature certain types of literature should be available and one must study and learn to use these. Each of these tools involve specific works. The most used are listed in the bibliography at the end of this text. The student must learn to use those available to him by completing the assignment that follows.

Nomenclator. – Lists of genera, citations to their original designation, and their date of publication are called nomenclators. A number of these are listed in the bibliography. Nomenclators are necessary to help prevent duplication of a generic name in the animal groups. Because a nomenclator is a closed source, it must be supplemented by current awareness sources such as *Zoological Record* and *Biological Abstracts.*

Catalog.—A catalog is a very specialized type of literature used as a closed retrieval system. The construction of a catalog is a detailed subject beyond the scope of the present volume. Because catalogs of insects vary so greatly, each one must be studied in some detail before it can be used properly. Several of the assignments at the end of this chapter require the use of catalogs and these are listed in the bibliography at the end of the volume.

TAXONOMIC LITERATURE TOOLS

Nomenclators
Catalogs
Zoological Record
Bibliographies

Zoological Record.—This specialized serial publication is the most useful information retrieval source for the taxonomist because it lists all new taxa for the period covered. The introduction contains references of use to the general entomologist, but there are no economic papers cited. The entire set of volumes of this work should be examined. Further details are given in chapters 7 and 8.

Bibliographies.—A bibliography of past literature is extremely useful for all types of retrospective search. Several of these are listed in the bibliography of this text.

Finally, remember that coding and retrieval involves not only the document profile, but the matching of a request profile with the document. When this involves names of organisms, it must include pertinent bibliographic information. To retrieve taxonomic literature, an extensive library is necessary. Many of the following assignments cannot be completed unless the available library has an extensive section on entomology, including complete sets of many periodicals.

ASSIGNMENT 5 (Cont.)

5.5 EARLY LITERATURE. Examine a copy of Linnaeus, 1758. Note the format. Look up the following names and make a proper 3 x 5 catalog card for each species. To do this assignment, it will be necessary to first determine the current assignment of these names. By means of a nomenclator, determine the order to which these species are assigned. By using a catalog of the order, locate the original citation to Linnaeus, and check in that volume: *Nacerdes melanura; Xylocopa virginica; Polyphylla Fullo; Dermestes lardarius.*

5.6 How many species were described in the genus *Oedemera* by 1800? This may be determined by using Sherborn (1902) and the Junk-Schenkling (1910-1940) catalog of Coleoptera.

5.7 NOMENCLATORS. You wish to describe a new genus and call it *Pseudoxacis.* Is this name available (i.e., never been used)? In your answer, give the steps you followed and cite the references consulted. Do the same with *Dido*, and *Nicrophorus.*

5.8 DATES OF PUBLICATION. Determine the exact date of publication of the following names: *Polyphylla decemlineata* (Say); *Oxacis minuta* Champion; *Ditylonia* Champion.

OPTIONAL INVESTIGATION

Determine from the library stamps or otherwise, (by reference to the literature on dates of publication, or published dates given in later issues of the journal), the exact date of publication of the last issue for the year 1944 of five North American entomological journals.

5.9 THE TYPE SPECIES OF GENERA. Give the following facts for each of the generic names listed below: 1) the exact reference to the original proposal; 2) list of originally included species, and 3) indicate what has to be done in each case to ascertain the type species of these genera: *Abbella; Biblio; Bledius; Dimecoenia; Hoplitalysia; Minagenia; Macremphylus; Pseudorhyssa; Pseudacysta; Pyrota; Seladonia; Tabanus; Teretriosoma; Thrimolus; Timulla.*

OPTIONAL INVESTIGATION

A recent revisor has erected a new subgenus of the genus *Oxacis* for all but one of the North American species of the old genus *Copidita.* He called the new subgenus *Oxycopis*, and later raised this subgenus to generic rank. When describing the new subgenus, he designated *Necydalis notoxoides* Fabricius as the type of the subgenus. *Probosca quadrimaculata* Motschulsky is the type of the genus *Copidita* because it was the only included species at the time of description. Why was *Oxycopis* necessary?

Determine the type species of the genera in the first list above, and give the reason for this designation [check copy of Code; this assignment may be completed only if the necessary literature giving type species designation is available in the library.]

5.10 HOMONYMY AND SYNONYMY. What relationships do the two follow-
ing names have to one another? *Trichofeltia* McDonnough, 1928 (April 1929),
Bulletin National Museum of Canada, no. 55 (Biological Series no. 16),A generic
revision of the North American agrotid moths, p. 61. *Trichofeltia* Barnes and
Benjamin, 1929 (June), Bulletin Brooklyn Entomological Society, v. 24, p. 177.
Explain.

Explain the following: *Fissilamoncodes* Neave, 1939 and *Fissilanoncodes* Pic,
1912. *Microps* Megerle, 1821 *in* Dejean (not Megerle *in* Dahl, 1823; Wagler,
1828; Stevens or Fischer-Waldheim, 1829; Wagler, 1830; Agassiz, 1833; Haliday,
1833; or Hallowell, 1865), Cat. Coleop.: 72.

In 1903, Charles Robertson of Carlinville, Illinois, described a new genus of
bees which he called *Antennaria* and in which he placed the following species:
Agapostemon coeruleum Smith, 1856; *Augochlora bicincta* Dahlbom, 1852;
Halictus antennatus Cresson, 1875; *Nomia bicolor* Lepeletier, 1845, and *Nomada
sanguinea* Say, 1823. Robertson made no definite statement as to which species
he considered the type species of the genus. Consequently in 1920, T. D. A.
Cockerell selected *Agapostemon coeruleum* Smith, 1856 as type of Robertson's
generic name because it was the first species included in the genus. But in 1924,
Miss Grace Sandhouse pointed out that this designation of *Agapostemon coeruleum* was invalid because in 1911, Heinrich Friese had removed *Agapostemon
coeruleum* Smith from *Antennaria* Robertson, 1903 and made it type species
of the new genus *Augochloropsis*. In other words, argued Miss Sandhouse, since
Agapostemon coeruleum Smith was no longer in *Antennaria* in 1920, as a con-
sequence of Friese's action, it was not available for designation by Cockerell as
type species of *Antennaria* in 1920. So in 1924, Miss Sandhouse selected *Nomada
sanguinea* Say, 1823 as the type species of *Antennaria* because it was the oldest
described species included by Robertson in his genus. Immediately, however, in
1925, H. F. Schwartz called attention to the fact that there is a very well known
genus of plants, belonging to the Compositae, named *Antennaria*; this was described by Gaertner in 1791. Inasmuch as Robertson's 1903 bee genus is a homonym of Gaertner's much older name, Schwartz renamed the bee genus *Robert-
sonia* and stated that the type species of the genus was *Nomia bicolor* Lepeletier,
1845. At present, there is little agreement among entomologists about what
generic name to use for this group, or what is the current type species of the
genus. What is the correct type species of the genus? Why? Show how to
catalog these names.

5.11 CATALOGS. Give the following facts for each of the species listed
below: a) name of describer; b) date of original description; c) exact reference to
original descriptions; d) genus in which species was placed when it was first

described; e) family to which the species belongs as given in the catalog or monograph consulted; f) catalog or monograph from which you obtained the reference:

Lytogaster abdominalis; Syntomosphyrum prionomeri; Bironella bironelli; Leptinotarsa lineola; Gypona antica; Acroleucas coxalis.

Give the following facts for each of the generic names listed below: a) name of describer; b) date of original proposal; c) exact reference to original proposal; d) if preoccupied, give author of preoccupying use and date.

Apamea; Argyroploce; Bombyx; Compsotata; Cressonia; Cryphia; Erana; Haemorrhagia; Mesolomia; Paramathia; Pseudobryomina.

5.12 Find out the names and affiliation of the current commissioners of the *International Commission of Zoological Nomenclature.*

REVIEW CHECKLIST

1. Why is coding analogous to the stating of a hypothesis?
2. Why is coding analogous to an identification of an organism?
3. Name several kinds of information codes.
4. List the five characteristics of a good index.
5. Define: information coding; document profile; index language; conceptual analysis; classification schedule; notation; class numbers; index terms; code terms; subject index; subject headings; controlled vocabulary.
6. What are the two factors in coding that prevent 100% retrieval?
7. What are the two steps involved in the information coding process?
8. Explain the need for a controlled vocabulary.
9. What is the use of the conceptual analysis? The thesaurus?
10. What are the current limitations of automatic indexing?
11. What does coding need for up-dating?
12. How are specimens treated in an IRS?
13. The International Code of Zoological Nomenclature is concerned with what subject? What does it NOT deal with in zoology?
14. What is meant by the law of priority?
15. What is the starting date for zoological nomenclature?
16. What is the distinctive feature of "Systema Naturae"?
17. What is meant by "early literature"?
18. What is the starting date of the current "code of nomenclature"? [Not the one now in effect, but the original one.]
19. What is the function of a holotype specimen?
20. Many species lack a holotype. What does the taxonomist do about this?
21. What is the relationship between the "Code" and "literature"?

22. All kinds of "types" are not valid. Give an example of one that is not and explain.

23. List three requirements for the validation of a generic name in 1965.

24. Give two ways a genus may be a synonym of another genus.

25. How is it determined that two species belong to the same genus?

26. Give the one way a species may be a synonym of another species.

27. If you find, through a misspelling of a generic name, in print, that this results in there being two identical generic names in the animal kingdom, what must be done?

28. Under what conditions can a homonym in two species-group taxa be restored to use?

29. Explain subjective, objective, primary, and secondary as these terms apply to synonyms and homonyms.

CHAPTER 7

SEARCH RESOURCES

A great variety of publications, catalogs, files, and indexes are available as *search resources*. All of these are designed to speed the location of documents and records. Most of them are produced in printed form because this is the easiest generally available production method. These printed volumes are merely published card files, and they, because of their hard form, are a closed system, always out of date, and frequently rather incomplete. Their use as a means of locating documents and records is limited.

Publications used primarily as reference sources may be issued periodically. Some of these are discussed in this chapter. Abstracts, indexes, and catalogs, also search resources, are discussed in following chapters. Still other search resources of a more general nature are found in the reference section of libraries and are not discussed here. Many of these are of use to the entomologists and new ones frequently become available. The student must brouse this section and obtain the help of the librarian to make best use of these facilities (see Katz, 1969 for further discussion of reference works, and Farrier, 1969 for other information.)

The coding procedure for documents discussed in chapter 6 is now used in reverse. A search request is designed to form a request profile. For example, if information about a species of insect is desired, the request profile is the code name (scientific name, or common name, or both) of the insect. However, information about this organism may be filed also under synonyms of the scientific name. So the formation of the search profile becomes more involved than it may seem at first. Search for topical information becomes even more complex when information about processes are required. The importance of the thesaurus as a means of coordinating the request profile and the code terms now become even more apparent.

In actual practice, the search for information may be rather haphazard. It often consists of little more than browsing titles, a time consuming, low retrieval, practice. When this is done it can only result in the overlooking of many useful documents. To improve upon this, one must consider every possible source of information. First, a study of the principal references is made. As this is done, a vocabulary with a list of synonyms is constructed. Additional documents will provide new words and the vocabulary is increased. The vocabularies for the CROSS index published by *Biological Abstracts* and the table of contents of *Zoological Record* serve as a good start and these publications form the basic reference list. Each project requires its own detailed list of terms to be used in making a request profile. These request terms become the code terms used to make a retrieval. Once the request terms are translated into the usable code terms by checking through the thesaurus the literature search can begin.

Various retrieval programs making use of modern search equipment are in operation, but few have been utilized to any extent outside of the organization producing the system. For example, a few organizations use the Electro-Writer to link information centers. However, except in industry, this is seldom used. No non-industrial application of the Xerox Telecopier is known to me. Its potential use in libraries seems to have escaped the attention of the Xerox Corporation. None are being used specificially for entomology, but a study is underway for this as mentioned previously, and a personalized program suitable for individuals or small organizations involving EDP equipment is described at the end of this chapter.

SOME SEARCH RESOURCES

Each of the types of search resources listed in the study box is described below followed with examples and discussion in the text. The reader is cautioned, however, that this list gives some typical examples only. Finding those needed for a particular project will require additional study by those making the information search.

TYPES OF SEARCH RESOURCES

Reference works
Card files
Lists of current literature
Abstracts and indexes
Special library holdings
CLASS and BA Previews (of BIOSIS)
Clearinghouse and Scientific Information Exchange

Elsewhere in this text emphasis has been placed on the use of card files as the principal search resource. There is no doubt about their continued use as an individual search method and as an index to library holdings. The beginning of all information retrieval is with the library file card catalog.

In an attempt to bring currently available literature to the attention of researchers, teachers, and students, it has been the practice of most periodicals to publish bibliographies and reviews of papers and books. Because there is no central register of available literature in biology or entomology, there is no way to tell the completeness of any listing, and because there are no rules for coding and publications are poorly coded, there is no way to determine the extent of the request profile that is developed from these listings. There deficiencies clearly make entomological information retrieval a haphazard venture.

Current Contents, Life Sciences (CCLS)®.—This is a weekly publication produced by the Institute for Scientific Information (ISI)*. It consists of reproductions of the table of contents of about 900 jour-

---

*325 Chestnut Street, Philadelphia, PA 19105.

nals, as a form of current awareness. Its greatest use is as a "browsing" device for a research biologist. It covers original source publications in biochemistry, medicine, botany, zoology, pharmacology, cytology, genetics, systematics, ecology, and other life science disciplines. One feature of interest is that the issues of CCLS bearing a table of contents of a journal may arrive before the journal itself reaches the reader. Each of the weekly issues of CCLS contains a computer-produced alphabetical index and address directory of the authors of papers noted in that issue. This feature is designed to make it easy for CCLS subscribers to request reprints without delay, a practice that should be discouraged if not eliminated for reasons elaborated upon in chapter 5. The greatest limitation of this publication is the dependence upon titles as information descriptors. We have already noted the weakness of titles. Still a further limitation is the omission of many important information sources so that this, like the others, becomes one more source to check.

The Quarterly Review of Biology. — This periodical published analytical reviews of books, texts, and monographs of nearly all phases of biology for decades. Recently the publication time lag, the restricted scope of the articles, and the opinionated personal nature of many of the reviews lessens the value of the publication. No attempt is made to code or abstract the publications reviewed, nor is there any indication of the extent of the coverage of the issues.

Book reviews are found in many entomological journals. Few of them are useful; the coverage is erratic, and the system is costly to publishers who are asked to supply a free book to each of these journals. Even with the various points of view and the several reviews that may be available for each publication, the system is not very effective. Recent attempts to find a wider group of specialists to act as reviewers for some journals have improved the reviews to some extent. The post publication reviews suffer from the same problems as the prepublication reviews (see chapter 5). One way the system might be improved is to devise an acceptable classification of topics and a comprehensive list of publications dealing with each topic. A reviewer might then be able to place a given work in its proper perspective and compare it logically with existing treatments of the same subjects. The *Book Review Index* (1965+, Gale Research Co., Detroit) is now the best source for review citations.

Various guides to the periodic literature are available but these are of a general nature and are of little help to the entomologist. *The Reader's Guide to Periodical Literature* is a good source for popular and semipopular articles, and, for some bibliographies, this resource may be necessary.

Science Citation Index®.—This is a current bibliographic search tool published by ISI. It provides, by the calendar year, a review of what has happened in a specific area of study by tracing citations. It is composed of four parts. In addition to the citations, there are the following indexes. The *Citation Index* is an alphabetical directory that shows, for each cited reference, subsequent works which cite it during the period indexed. The *Source Index* gives the titles of the cited articles and complete bibliographic information. It is essentially a calendar year author index used to identify all the papers published by a specific author in the period indexed. The *Permuterm*® *Subject Index* is used also to lead researchers to the papers published in the period indexed. It is produced by a system of permuted pairs, computer-processed terms derived from titles and sub-titles of articles and listed alphabetically with every other associated term.

BA-Previews.—This is a tape record (but without the abstracts) of the contents of *Biological Abstracts* and *Bioresearch Index*. It is supplied by BIOSIS approximately six weeks in advance of the regular printed edition of *Biological Abstracts*. The tape is a 9-track, 800 bits-per-inch variable record length and variable block length tape which gives a print-out with the following elements: 1) volume number of *Biological Abstracts* and *Bioresearch Index*; 2) abstract or bibliographic reference number; 3) *Coden* and primary journal abbreviation; 4) primary journal volume number, issue number, inclusive pagination, and year of issue; 5) title enriched by the addition as supplementary words of appropriate terms to indicate contents; 6) author; 7) numeric codes for subject headings in the CROSS index and taxonomic entries in the *Biosystematic Index* (see chapter 8 for further details about *Biological Abstracts* and associated BIOSIS publications).

C.L.A.S.S.—A new individualized current awareness search service is now available from BIOSIS. The *acronym* CLASS is an abbreviation for *Current Literature Alerting Search Service*. It is a selective dissemination of information search service used after the publication, unlike *Data Documents*, of the primary publication, which provides this type of service at the time of publication. CLASS is a product of computer processing, based upon *BA-Previews*, the magnetic tape service of BIOSIS (described above). The subscriber selects as many descriptors as he desires. Once these are selected the service begins. To aid in the development of a profile of descriptors BIOSIS provides a subject classification outline. Two computer print-outs per month are provided, a total of six computer passes. An average of twenty hits (references that match the search request) per computer pass, or 40 per month is considered the average maximum without additional charge.

In addition to the private agencies mentioned above, two governmental agencies provide services of interest to the entomologist. The *Clearinghouse for Scientific and Technical Information (CFSTI)* is an agency within the Department of Commerce that processes government and other organizationally generated reports. They produce a monthly list of available documents. Its holdings on biological subjects are relatively low at present, but they are being rapidly expanded.

The second service is the *Science Information Exchange*. This is a list and description of all funded research projects. Users may request project descriptions by subject and receive copies of each pertinent description. These list the title, investigators, location of research project, description, and supporting agency.

Special library holdings, both private and public, are an important search resource because they are created for a specific project or series of projects. These libraries include out-of-print books, often rare books, reprints, xerox copies, manuscripts, and files for a special project.

Often times large private libraries are built, particularly by insect taxonomists. Many of these scientists have bibliophilic interests as a natural adjunct of their taxonomic interests. Thus special libraries, often of considerable value are created. Books and reprints for these libraries are obtained from antiquarian book dealers, a few of whom either specialize in entomological literature, or have a large stock of old entomological books. A list of dealers as well as publishers is given in Appendix II.

Special references are available for some entomological topics. For the principal ones, refer to the topics in the bibliography, Appendix I.

Among the types of reference works used as entomological search resources are: *bibliographies*; encyclopedias; handbooks (see chapter 9); dictionaries; glossaries, and geographical references (gazetteers).

ASSIGNMENT 6

6.1 Visit the library and examine each of the available search resources described in this chapter. Note for each the entomological content. Describe the extent of usefulness to the entomologist of each of these.

More than the above literature references are available. Practice in using these may be gained by completing the following exercises. Make correct bibliographic author entries for the following publications:

1. Girault, Ent. News, Dec. 1903, p. 323.
2. Kalmus, Proc. Ent. Soc. London, Ser. A, 1945, p. 84.
3. McDonnough, Can. Ent., July-August 1946, p. 147.
4. The family Formicidae in the Hymenoptera of America North of Mexico, 1952.
5. The Lepidoptera section of the list of the insects of New York.
6. The Elateridae part of the Junk catalog.
7. British Lepidoptera - Tutt.
8. Schoder's Handbuch der Entomologie.

ELEMENTS OF A RETRIEVAL

Both manual and machine searches for information have essentially the same elements and as we have seen, the request profile must match the document profile. Both sets of descriptors must coincide. This is a coding-decoding procedure, and the operator of the system must keep this in mind because no machine process has been devised yet to perform this operation. Reference to the flow chart of information retrieval (figure 3, page 24) shows that search requests are processed in exactly the same manner, as are the documents, to produce a request profile. The difference is that the request must be processed with the project description at hand as the complement of the document.

The actual retrieval procedure whether planned or conducted at random, manual, or by machine, consists of the following steps:

1. The formulation of the search request. This may be a simple question, e.g., what species of Oedemeridae are known to occur in Arizona?; or what kind of sound is produced by stored grain beetles? These questions are a part or all of a research project, and the search request begins the literature or information search described in chapter 1.

2. After preliminary study has been made of the topics involved, an analysis of the subject content is begun. It is obvious that no retrieval will be made using the exact words of the original research question if a needed research project is undertaken. In other words, there would be no need for the research if the literature search produced the answer to the research question. One of the reasons for a literature survey, however, is to determine whether or not previous research has answered the questions in part or entirely. This may have been done, but reported using different terms so that it has gone unrecognized by the person asking the question.

3. A conceptual analysis to show the interrelationship of subtopics is necessary to provide and increase the terms to use during the search. If the project is a taxonomic one, this step is comparable to the formation of a taxonomic catalog. The synonyms in the catalog show the various terms that might be used as a part of the request profile. Other projects have the equivalent in the different set of terms or combination of terms used to describe the phenomenon. The arrangement of these terms show the synonyms and help to show the concept one has of the phenomenon. For example, a search request for information on "pollen-feeding Coleoptera" might have to be modified to "physiology of Coleoptera, especially pollen-feeding" in order to find the literature that contains information on this subject. Other arrangements are possible.

4. Once the analysis has been completed, the results must be translated into index terms. If a thesaurus has been prepared then the appropriate index term may be easily determined. These terms form the request profile that must be matched with the document profiles for a retrieval. In a manual retrieval this is a matter of making the search with this variety of terms.

After some reflection and a few attempts to look-up information it becomes apparent that the lack of a proper match of the request profile and the document profile may result in a low retrieval or in a deluge of useless references. It is also true that the current methods of information dissemination, lacking as they do, critical analysis of content, are likely to provide an inefficient means of retrieval, and this, in turn, results in information loss.

RETROSPECTIVE SEARCH

All information services known to me are primarily concerned with current awareness, that is, they find it sufficient, under current conditions of the information deluge, to bring to the user the daily accumulation of information about his particular special interests. This is never enough, for no matter what branch of entomology concerns the researcher or student, he must make use of a considerable number of works published prior to the inception of search services. A review of the back literature is termed a retrospective search. Except for taxonomy, this seldom involves more than about 30 years of the past literature. Unfortunately taxonomists are involved with literature back to 1758. The primitive search methods and demands for detail, as explained in chapter 6, are exceedingly time consuming and of doubtful value. The philosophy of this is beyond the present study. Retrospective search for taxonomy is aided by the taxonomic catalogs that are available. Other entomological topics are best searched by the citation method. This is done by checking bibliographies of recent papers which in turn refer to previous work, these to still earlier works, and so on. In this way it is possible to compile a workable bibliography. There is no efficient system of checking such a bibliography for completeness. One can only hope that an important work has not been omitted. Fortunately the abstract and index publications, *Biological Abstracts* and *Zoological Record*, cover the recent past with sufficient thoroughness to prevent in most cases the duplication of current research efforts.

A MACHINE PROGRAMMED RETRIEVAL SYSTEM

Machine information retrieval programming is a subject of considerable current interest and research (see SATCOM recommendations E5 and E8). I do not intend to lengthen this text by becoming involved with computer programming. However, a relatively simple program has been developed and tested in my class. It may be used by an individual or a small group. This program is reproduced and briefly described here. It may be used for the storage and retrieval of any type of document that can be coded and stored. This includes documents pertaining to phenomena as well as organisms. For information retrieval involving organisms, machine retrieval search requests must be designed so that no biological information is required and no taxonomic judgement is needed. The present program meets this need by permitting the coding of documents or records using all of the names that might apply to an organism. The request may be phrased to drop references to information stored under any or all of these names. The program as reproduced here (Fig. 8) is for the CDC 6500 computer. The deck assembly is shown (Fig. 9) and a sample retrieval showing information about organisms (Fig. 10). The same sort of retrieval is made from a stored taxonomic catalog where the names of the organisms form the code words and are arranged in catalog sequence as citation cards.

ASSIGNMENT 6 (Cont.)

6.2 Following the format for the machine retrieval program given here (Figs. 8 and 9), prepare punch cards for each of your coded 3 x 5 reference cards used for assignment 5.3. Test the program by making an actual retrieval request.

REVIEW CHECKLIST

1. Define: acronym; coden; search profile; search resources.
2. What are the general categories of search resources?
3. What is the difference between a search request and a request profile?
4. Why is the search pattern often haphazard?
5. What are the specific types of search resources? Give examples of each.
6. What are the four elements of a retrieval?
7. What is meant by a retrospective search? What are the difficulties of making this kind of search? List some helpful sources for retrospective search.
8. How does a machine search differ from a manual search?
9. What are the two kinds of machine searches that may be useful for entomologists?

```
C        THIS RETRIEVAL ALGORITHM WAS WRITTEN IN ITS ORIGINAL FORM
C        BY D. L. JAMESON, 1969, BIOSCIENCE 19:232-233 AND WAS ADAPTED
C        FOR THE CDC 6500 BY R. L. GIESE (PURDUE UNIVERSITY) AS
C        PROGRAM 'FORENT 625' *SEARCH*.
         PROGRAMSEARCH(INPUT,OUTPUT,TAPE5=INPUT,TAPE6=OUTPUT)
         DIMENSION ISEEK(7),LABEL(8),LIST(69)
     101 FORMAT(2I2,8A8)
     102 FORMAT(8A8)
     103 FORMAT(I1,69A1)
     104 FORMAT(1X,69A1)
     105 FORMAT(////50HTHE CATEGORIES IN THE SEARCH LIST ARE AS FOLLOWS:
        5      //7(1X,1A8),/)
     106 FORMAT(
        661HTHE NUMBER OF CATEGORIES REQUIRED TO MATCH BEFORE LISTING IS
        6 ,I2//20X,15(1H*))
     107 FORMAT(1X)
C        A SIMPLE ALGORITHM FOR A PERSONALIZED CITATION SEARCH
C        NC=NUMBER OF CATEGORIES REQUIRED TO LIST
C        NI=NUMBER OF CATEGORIES IN SEARCH LIST
C        ISEEK=LIST OF CATEGORIES USING FIRST EIGHT LETTERS
C            OF EACH WORD
C        LABEL=CATEGORY LIST OF EACH CITATION USING
C            FIRST EIGHT LETTERS OF EACH WORD
C        IL=NUMBER OF MATCHING CATEGORIES
C        IEND=LAST CARD INDICATOR FOR CITATION
C
C        READ THE SEARCH TERMS
       1 READ(5,101)NC,NI,ISEEK
       2 WRITE(6,105)ISEEK
         WRITE(6,106)NC
C
C        READ INDEX TERMS
       3 READ(5,102)LABEL
         IF(EOF,5)16,4
C
C        COMPARE SEARCH TERMS TO INDEX TERMS
       4 IL=0
       5 DO 8 I=1,NI
       6 DO 8 L=1,7
       7 IF(ISEEK(I).EQ.LABEL(L))IL=IL+1
       8 CONTINUE
       9 IF(IL-NC)10,13,13
C
C        NO MATCH, LOOK FOR THE NEXT CITATION
      10 READ(5,103)IEND
      11 IF(IEND)16,10,3
C
C        MATCH, WRITE OUT THE CITATION
      13 WRITE(6,107)
      99 READ(5,103)IEND,LIST
      14 WRITE(6,104)LIST
      15 IF(IEND)16,99,3
      16 STOP
         END
```

Fig. 8. Program "Search" adapted to the CDC 6500 computer.

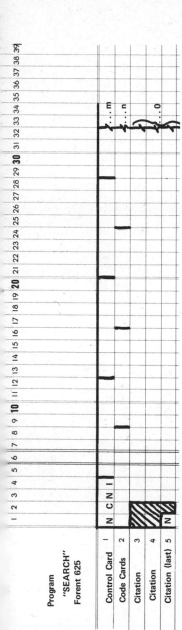

Fig. 9. The deck assembly for program "Search".

1. CONTROL CARDS

Col. 1-2 NC= The number of categories listed on the control card search list the user wants matched on the citation cards to allow the citation to be listed (right hand justified).

Col. 3-4 NI= The number of categories listed on the search list (right hand justified).

Col. 5-12 This is the search request containing 8 letter words the user wants to compare to the citations. m=9 and

13-20 each word must be 8 bits long (completed with blanks if necessary).

…m

2. CODE CARD

Col. 1-80 The first card of each citation must contain one or more categories which the user defines as representing the content of the citation. n=10 and each key word must contain 8 digits.

3. CITATION CARDS

Col. 3-80 Any number of citation cards may be used to include author, title, year and a summary if desirable. Leave the first two columns blank except for the last card in the citation. The last card has any number greater than 0 in the first column.

DECK ASSEMBLY

1. Account card - for computer center accounts. 2. Monitor cards - as required by the computer center. 3. "789" card - as a signal card. 4. Program deck (see figure 8). 5. "789" card - as a signal card. 6. Data cards - the citation cards in 2 and 3 above may be repeated any number of "times, i.e., the user can have any number of citations each headed with a code card (this is the "information bank"). 7. "6789" card - as a stop card.

THE CATEGORIES IN THE SEARCH LIST ARE AS FOLLOWS:

POPULATI MORTALIT DYNAMICS

THE NUMBER OF CATEGORIES REQUIRED TO MATCH BEFORE LISTING IS   1

****

MORRIS,R.F. 1957. THE INTERPRETATION OF MORTALITY DATA IN STUDIES
ON POPULATION DYNAMICS. CAN. ENTOMOL. 89:49-69

MORRIS,R.F. AND C.A. MILLER. 1954. THE DEVELOPMENT OF LIFE
TABLES FOR THE SPRUCE BUDWORM. CAN.J.ZOOL. 32:283-301.

FLANDERS,S.E. AN M.E.BADGLEY. 1963. PREY-PREDATOR INTERACTIONS
IN SELF-BALANCED LABORATORY POPULATIONS.HILGARDIA 35:145-183

WELLINGTON,W.G. 1965. AN APPROACH TO A PROBLEM IN POPULATION
DYNAMICS. QUESTIONES ENTOMOL. 1:175-186.

VARLEY,G.C. 1957. MEANING OF DENSITY DEPENDENCE AND RELATED TERMS
IN POPULATION DYNAMICS. NATURE 181:1778-1781.

HARCOURT,D.G. 1963. MAJOR MORTALITY FACTORS IN THE POPULATION
DYNAMICS OF THE DIAMONDBACK MOTH, PLUTELLA MACULIPENNIS (CURT.)
(LEPIDOPTERA:PLUTELLIDAE). MEM. ENTOMOL. SOC. CAN.32:55-66.

DEMPSTER,J.P. 1963. THE POPULATION DYNAMICS OF GRASSHOPPERS
AND LOCUSTS. BIOL. REV. 38:490-529.

Fig. 10. A sample retrieval using "Search" for information about organisms.

CHAPTER 8

ABSTRACTS AND INDEXES

Certain kinds of search resources are not discussed in the previous chapter because of their complex nature. Two are of particular use to all entomologists and are discussed in detail here. Abstracting and indexing services for functional biology are currently provided principally by *Biological Abstracts*, which also includes taxonomy. Taxonomic zoology, including entomology, is indexed by *Zoological Record*. Both publications have some time lag; *Biological Abstracts* from 3 to 18 months, while *Zoological Record* is always 3 to 5 years behind. More federal funds have been recommended for the production of this kind of literature access service (SATCOM recommendation C1).

Even abstracts and indexes need repackaging to make them more useful. BIOSIS is providing two of these now, *Abstracts of Mycology* and *Abstracts of Entomology,* and is considering others. The *Guide to the World's Indexing and Abstracting Services in Science and Technology* lists over 1,800 such services. This is bewildering information to anyone who believes that he should know what information is already available before he generates more.

The aim of abstracts and indexes published as current awareness documents is to make it possible for any person or group of persons to keep up with the literature on their own narrow branch or division of a discipline. According to the questionnaires returned to the Entomological Society of America, the following publications, in the order presented, are the most used by entomologists:

BIOLOGICAL ABSTRACTS
BIBLIOGRAPHY OF AGRICULTURE
ZOOLOGICAL RECORD
REVIEW OF APPLIED ENTOMOLOGY
   SERIES A, AGRICULTURE
   SERIES B, MEDICAL AND VETERNARY
PESTICIDES DOCUMENT BULLETIN
INDEX OF AMERICAN ECONOMIC ENTOMOLOGY
   (Discontinued)
PESTICIDES MONITORING JOURNAL
AGRICULTURAL ABSTRACTS

Although none of these are complete for their special topics, their retrieval efficiency is high. They are invaluable for entomological research and are necessary for the literature search at the beginning of any project. *Biological Abstracts* and *Zoological Record* require detailed study for their use. The others are less systematized, but follow the same principles as these.

THE NATURE OF ABSTRACTS AND ABSTRACT WRITING

Abstracts are of three types, although some may combine features in such a way that it may be difficult to determine which of the three they are. An *indicative abstract* (descriptive abstract) describes the original document but does not contain data itself; an *informative abstract* summarizes the main facts, ideas, and conclusions, the details of which are in the original document. This type of abstract is the most useful. Variations of this may be used in Data Documents, and other short forms of publication. A *critical abstract* (evaluative abstract) is more of a review than the others because it attempts to evaluate or assess the value of the original document. This type of abstract is for special purposes and is not generally a part of information retrieval.

The correct method of informative abstract writing for biology is described in a guide prepared by BIOSIS. However, several problems exist in attempting to select the proper data to include in this condensed form. In general, an abstract should be no longer than 3% of the original article, written as a completely independent article by itself. That is, there should be no need to refer to the original article to determine the meaning of the abstract. If the article is to be consulted it is for details only. The entire abstract should be no more than 1600 characters, or approximately 150 to 300 words (20 punch cards) if the abstract is to be used for storage in an ADP system. Taxonomic papers are particularly difficult to abstract, especially those with a large number of included species. It is generally thought that new taxa should be listed, but this is because the process of abstract writing is confused with indexing. Unless enough information is given to recognize a new taxon, it need not be mentioned, but the taxon in the next highest category may be mentioned with an indication of the number of taxa of the lower category discussed and/or first recognized as undescribed.

ASSIGNMENT 7

7.1 Examine several abstracts in one or more periodicals and note which of the three types they are. Find an example of each of these. Make a xeroxed copy of each; then, at the top of a separate sheet type each article citation. Paste the xeroxed copy of the abstract of the article beneath the citation. With the help of the original article, redo each of the abstracts following the guide supplied by BIOSIS.

INDEXING

The characteristics of an index have been discussed in chapter 6, page 88, but the actual procedure for indexing was not discussed in detail. Several types of indexes are now in use. One kind is a set of words arranged alphabetically, usually at the end of a book or a volume of a journal. Page numbers complete the input-output pairs. These numbers tell the user the page or pages containing further information. This index may contain all three types of information, i.e., terms refering to topics, names of people (usually authors), and names of organisms. In large works it is often more convenient to provide two or even three indexes for these separate kinds of indexed matter.

A second kind of index, only recently adopted by periodicals, is a set of code terms or descriptors for each article. These terms are usually supplied by the author and appear at the end of the abstract. This provides a set of terms that are usable in abstracting and indexing periodicals as well as the index to the volume. Unfortunately, no uniform system or set of rules has been devised to follow when doing this. The *Style Manual for Biological Journals* specifies that "up to ten" words may be used but gives no reason for this limitation.

A third kind of index appears as a separate publication. *Zoological Record* is the best example of this. Here all new and changed scientific names are indexed with full references to the publication, and an indication of the position of the indexed taxon in the classification. The country, state, or province of new species is given to show those working on a restricted fauna the area covered. Further indexing by topic is given only by reference to the document (see further discussion of this below). Other types of indexes are available.

The *Uniterm* system of indexing, and other systems (such as the "Automatic indexing of personal bibliographies" system proposed by Bridges, 1970) have been devised for use in small, special, or personal libraries. The Uniterm system apparently was devised by Documentation, Inc. and announced in 1955. The procedure involves setting up separate cards for each index term used. Documents are numbered consecutively; this number is then used as the reference to the document. Numbered items need not be confined to separate items, but may be used to refer to articles in journals, even those not in the special library. Coding of documents consists of underlining the key words in the title and addition of any others necessary to use as a notation. The document number is entered on each of the term cards corresponding with the underlined words. To facilitate finding a number on the card ten columns are drawn or printed on the cards, one for each of the possible last digits of the reference number. The document numbers are entered in the proper column.

The advantage of this system is the ease in which the document may be indexed in detail. One disadvantage is that no arrangement of documents, other than in numerical sequence is permitted without further coding of the reference number. It is possible that a scheme of locators could be devised by keeping a list of document numbers in a notebook and a notation as to the location of each after the document number. This would be especially helpful if articles in other libraries are included in the indexing system. The most serious disadvantage is the single term. This may require far more listings than is practical. For example, the uniterm "biology" may be listed hundreds of times. A binominal system employing topical hierarcy would improve upon this system, but this has not yet been devised.

Indexing is usually left as a final chore for an author. He writes names and page numbers on slips of paper as he reads through the final page proof. These are later arranged alphabetically and produced as the final portion of a book, pamphlet, or rarely for a long article in a journal (refer to chapter 6 for the characteristics of a good index). The Uniterm system might be adapted to this indexing as a useful way to document data and reference sources.

USE OF BIOLOGICAL ABSTRACTS AND RELATED PUBLICATIONS

BIOSIS provides detailed instructions for the use of their publications in the introductory pages of each issue, and also as a separate booklet: *Guide to the Indexes for Biological Abstracts and Bioresearch Index.* These should be consulted.

Of the several publications of BIOSIS, *Biological Abstracts* is the main and most comprehensive periodical, and the most used. It contains the actual abstracts of reported documents arranged by topic. Each abstract is numbered and full reference to the original article is given. No abstract number is duplicated during the calendar year, but each new year the numbering is started again. The number is used as a reference in each of the various indexes. No coding or indexing is given with the abstract, but four indexes are provided with each issue (see following list). The coding for the various indexes is done from the title, from words contained in the abstract, or from words added by the editors. Twenty-four issues of *Biological Abstracts* appear each year.

In addition to the complete *Biological Abstracts, B.A.S.I.C. (Biological Abstracts Subjects in Context)* is published separately for wider, individual, circulation. This is a computer arranged subject index compiled from significant terms in the titles of the publications abstracted. Key terms may be added by the BIOSIS staff. These search terms are computer permuted and arranged alphabetically. Titles of research papers written in a language other than English are translated into

English. This permutation of the title allows each significant term to be used for a possible retrieval. The abstract number provides the reference. Needless to say this is an extremely useful current awareness publication, but it is not exhaustive because it is not possible to index each term contained in the original document.

The *Bioresearch Index* is relatively new and provides a much needed index to non-journal literature. It is published monthly as a complete bibliography of the following types of literature: symposia; reviews; published letters; notes; bibliographies; preliminary reports; semi-popular journals; trade journals; annual institutional reports; selected governmental reports, and selected secondary sources. In addition, this publication contains its own B.A.S.I.C., but it does not contain abstracts of any of the publications listed.

The remaining publications of BIOSIS are: *Abstracts of Mycology,* a special selection of reprinted abstracts on mycology previously published in *Biological Abstracts; Abstracts of Entomology,* a publication similar to the preceding; the *Annual Cumulative Indexes* from *Biological Abstracts* and *Bioresearch Index; Biological Abstracts Annual list of serials,* a complete list of publications abstracted during the year; and *BA Previews* (magnetic tapes) mentioned in the previous chapter.

The four indexes provided with each issue of *Biological Abstracts* and *Bioresearch Index* referred to previously are 1) B.A.S.I.C., the subject index described above; 2) author index, and index to each author of papers abstracted; 3) the *Biosystematic Index,* a taxonomic guide to the papers abstracted, and 4) the *CROSS Index* (Computer Rearrangement Of Subject Specialities). The latter is referred to as a subject coordinator. Under subject headings, reference numbers are arranged in ten vertical columns according to the last digit in the number. This number appears under every relevant subject heading (as in Uniterm). By the use of this index very specific information may be obtained about a reference by comparing numbers listed under various subject headings. This permits further narrowing of the reference list before consulting the abstracts themselves. The *CROSS Index* has limited use in entomology because the taxonomic categories are too broad to be useful in a group as large as the insects.

ASSIGNMENT 7 (Cont.)

7.2 Obtain a copy of the "Guide to the indexes for Biological Abstracts and

Bioresearch Index" and complete the work sheet given in this publication.

USE OF ZOOLOGICAL RECORD

Zoological Record, founded in 1864, is published annually in 20 sections. The first section is concerned with zoology in general. The following sections treat a separate phylum or group of phyla, or in the case of the Insecta, a class. Section 20 is a list of new genera and sub-genera. By far the largest section is number 13, the section for insects. This is prepared by the Commonwealth of Entomology and not by the Zoological Society of London, the publisher of the other parts. Our concern here is with section 13.

The volume (section) is divided into three parts: 1) author, title, journal citation list (bibliography) for the year; 2) the subject index;* 3) the systematic index arranged alphabetically by order, family, and genus. The latter part contains only information of a purely taxonomic nature. All other information must be located in the second part of the index. No abstracts are published. Papers written entirely from an economic point of view are not included, but these are abstracted in the *Review of Applied Entomology*. Very short papers are noted in the index where the complete reference is also given, but it is not included in part one in the list of titles.

This index has served the taxonomists well for over 100 years. Unfortunately, it is always three or four years behind the current literature. Much could be done to imporve this situation, but not without greater expense.

ASSIGNMENT 7 (Cont.)

7.3 Select a genus of interest to you and by reference to "Zoological Record" record any changes that have been made since the last published catalog of the genus.

7.4 Select some restricted topic of interest to you and prepare a bibliography of references to this subject as listed in the past ten issues of "Zoological Record."

*The terms used in the subject index are reproduced in this text in chapter 6, page 93.

REVIEW CHECKLIST

1. What are the two principal sources of current references for non-economic entomology?

2. Name several other sources used by entomologists.

3. What publications are of most use to the economic entomologist?

4. What is the principal deficiency of all of these publications?

5. What degree of completeness might be expected for these publications? Overlap?

6. Name and define the three types of abstracts.

7. Give three essential elements of an abstract.

8. Why are taxonomic papers difficult to abstract?

9. Why is an index referred to as "input-output pairs"? What relationship does this have to "retrieval"?

10. Name and define the several different kinds of indexes.

11. Name some advantages and some disadvantages to "Uniterm" as an index. How might it be improved?

12. What are the several publications of BIOSIS?

13. What are two basic differences between "Zoological Record" and "Biological Abstracts"?

14. What are the four indexes used by "Biological Abstracts"?

15. What area is covered by "Biological Abstracts"?

16. When did "Biological Abstracts" start?

17. What are the three sections of "Zoological Record"?

18. What amount of overlap might you expect between "Biological Abstracts" and "Zoological Record"?

19. What area is covered by "Zoological Record"?

20. When did "Zoological Record" start?

21. What difficiencies are to be found in these two publications?

CHAPTER 9

SYNTHESIZED DATA

The term "synthesized data" is used here to include all kinds of publications that are not original documents or search resources. These documents or records are formed by the reprocessing of information. The distinction is not clearcut because original documents have a certain amount of reprocessed data as background information for the new research reported. Also, many taxonomic reports considered to be original documents contain a high percentage of previously available data presented in reprocessed form. Therefore, it is obvious that these distinctions have little value except as a means of becoming aware of the types of available information as an aid to the circumscription of a given body of knowledge. To be very critical of the current situation, if much of the data that is currently filling our journals were held back until it could be presented in a usable form, there would be less of a need for synthesized data publications, and less of an information explosion.

As it is, there is a great need for reprocessed data as the result of the overwhelming flood of information. Most of the publication energies since World War II have been devoted to the production of original documents. If societies would conserve their assets by developing a program of Data Documents or similar selective dissemination of information systems, more backing could be given to the publication of monographs, handbooks, manuals, and catalogs (see SATCOM recommendation B5, part 1).

SYNTHESIZING INFORMATION

Recent studies have brought out the importance of scientists devoting time to sifting, reviewing, and synthesizing information. These reviewers should be given the time and reward for performing such services, including grant support. This type of publishing is termed information reprocessing. Professional societies should be concerned with this in addition to the production of original documents (SATCOM recommendation B12).

If it were economically feasible, each worker ideally should have available to him a retrieval system that would automatically consolidate all of the accumulated information of particular interest to him, much the same as is done in space-age stories on TV. In the place of this, at the present time, review summaries can be prepared, especially for those concerned with the application of this scattered knowledge. This should be a part of every major research program and funds for the research should provide for this reprocessing (see SATCOM recommendation B3). These reviews need to be indexed and cataloged for ready access (SATCOM recommendations B4 and B13).

PROBLEMS OF SYNTHESIS

The work of compiling review articles, catalogs, and manuals is often regarded as something to be done by those incapable of doing original, creative work. This attitude is unfortunate because it prevents the production of this much needed product. Careful thought must be given to the compiling of working tools of this kind because of the need for great accuracy as well as the ability to organize, filter, and create a useful package of information. Contrary to popular belief, it is this kind of literature that is long lasting and brings great personal satisfaction.

One of the generally recognized omissions in most reprocessed data packs is negative data of seemingly poor quality work. We often hear about the need for a journal of negative results, but nothing is ever done to bring these data to the attention of researchers. This omission, without a doubt, has caused a great amount of expensive duplication of work.

Entomology lacks major attempts to produce a comprehensive synthesis of its data. The great number of species involved has prohibited, to date, any attempts to produce a world review of all groups. One of the greatest needs today is a world treatment of the insect pests. It is astounding that none is available! No one knows how many or even what species of insects are pests, and no one seems overly concerned about it. Yet the United States Department of Agriculture spends large sums of money each year to prevent the importation of insects and they do not know whether the intercepted species are potentially pests and have *no way to find out!*

The remainder of this chapter deals with the various kinds of synthesis publications that are possible. Many of those available are listed under their class in the bibliography.

REVIEWS

Several kinds of publications are called *reviews*. The three major types are defined below.

Periodical review. – The synthesis of a limited subject area covering a particular time interval is termed a periodical review. It presents the findings with little or no actual analysis. Such reviews are seldom used in entomology.

Ocassional review. – This kind of review discusses a subject broadly and interpretively and need not cover all literature during a clearly defined period. The review is selective and critical. This is the kind of review that is likely to appear in current status series (see below).

Analytical review. – Sometimes a book length analysis of concepts and theories dealing with a particular subject, clarifying and pinpointing areas needing investigation, appear. This type of review is badly needed but seldom has been produced for entomologists.

TAXONOMIC REVIEW

Often times the taxonomist finds it necessary to pause in his work and bring together the species of a genus or the genera of a family as a review of the extent of the group in number of species, their distribution, and their identification. This kind of review has a key for the identification of the genera and species, a brief diagnosis of the taxa, and notes on the distribution and biology, if known, of the group. It lacks the details of a revision and the finality of a monograph. It is my opinion that all taxonomic publications should be no *less* than a review or a supplement to a review. All other lesser contributions are likely to be unusable raw data and if they must be published, they should be treated as Data Documents. No clearcut distinction between a taxonomic review and a taxonomic revision has been made, and integrades occur in the literature.

REVISIONS AND MONOGRAPHS

Taxonomy has special types of literature that combine original documents and synthesis publications. Much of the taxonomic literature appears either as revisions or as monographs.

Revisions.–A *revision* is characterized by including more detailed data than the review. It is meant to bring together details needed as archival records in addition to the information for identification. The revisor selects a group of insects with a suitable number of species covering a more or less natural area; the species may or may not have been previously described. The information on the group is scattered in the literature and species can be identified for the most part either with difficulty or not at all. The revisor's chore is to assemble these species, write detailed descriptions as well as diagnoses, construct usable keys, record distribution and biological information, and present a definitive classification of the group. As a rough estimate, the average revision involves probably about 50 species. This could be a genus, a tribe, a subfamily, or even a family. This is not to imply that there are no larger or smaller revisions. Sometimes many hundreds of species are revised, and other times only a few. However, a revisor generally is able to restrict the size of his revision by selecting the category and the geographical area to conform to the size work load he desires. If a group should involve a complex speciation problem, fewer species are attempted than otherwise. Obviously there are no set rules governing this. The available time allotted to the research and the access to specimens and/or field data determine the size of the group selected for revision. The same principles govern the selection of the area to be covered. Usually revisions are regional, i.e., cover a section of the total range of the group. We sometimes see so-called "World" revisions, but since no species inhabits the entire world, all this means is that the entire group is covered. More restricted coverage is based on some political area usually because it is too difficult to assemble specimens from all regions, but also because of practicality. A revision for a particular region may be more useful than for another, and to include all areas might make the work too large for easy use. For example, it may be convenient to treat the species of the United States, or eastern United States, or even a single state. Works restricted to a single state are generally less useful because we seldom know enough about the distribution of a group to make a useful list of the species. However, some states have compiled records for a sufficient number of years so that there is a good chance that the species that actually occur within the political limits of the state are known. If there is sufficient demand, which there seldom is, then a state revision is warranted.

The most diagnostic feature of a revision is its format. These documents usually start with a brief history of the classification of the group (the literature search), followed by a diagnosis and description of the major taxon (e.g., family, subfamily, etc.). A key to the subdivisions of the major taxon is given, followed by diagnoses and descriptions of each of the included taxa in hierarchical order to species. Each species discussed includes information on its distribution. If there is a geographical restriction to the revision, notes on the total range and number of included species are given for each taxon above the category species. If the species has a wider range than that of the area covered by the revision, the entire range of the species is indicated. Notes and information on the biology are included in a separate section. Sometimes immature stages are described if they differ widely from the adults. Each species is followed by a section listing the specimens examined and their collection data.

This format for a revision has many variations. There are no rules that govern this because each group must be treated according to its particular requirements. One rule that should be enforced by editors (but isn't), is that a revision be useful by itself and not require the user to do additional work before he can use the information. In other words, a revision should be self-contained and written for use, not as an archival record of compiled data. The diagnoses, keys, illustrations, and other features should be presented so that the informed nonspecialist can turn to the work if he is interested and use it without the need to refer to other papers.

Monographs.—The only readily discernable difference between a revision and a monograph in taxonomic literature is the amount of archival information. A monograph reviews all available information on a particular group and records this information in a single work. These are sometimes called *memoirs* or *treatises*, but these terms are seldom used today. The term monograph is generally applied to any complete treatment of a particular topic, including taxonomic groups as well as functional subjects. A monograph reviews all of the past literature, arranges all of the information into a logical order or a classification and adds any new information available. If the document is done well, there is no further need to refer to any of the previous literature once the monograph is available. Very few entomological works may be identified as monographs.

OTHER FORMS OF SYNTHESIZED DATA

Bibliography.—It is often useful to compile a *bibliography* of references. These may be of several types. The most frequent is a bibliography of a particular person. Individual scientists often keep an up-to-date bibliography of their own writings as evidence of their accomplishments. These are published after their death as a part of their obituary. Biographies of living authors with an indication of the subject matter of their publications is given in *American Men of Science* and similar biographical works (see bibliography at the end of this volume). Extensive bibliographies are published with a revision or a monograph. Sometimes these may appear as separate works, for example, the bibliography of entomology from 1758 to 1863 by Horn and Schenkling (see bibliography at the end of this book). A third type of bibliography is that published by an institution or a society as a list of works published by them. A book seller or publisher's catalog is of this same category. Bibliographies are most useful as references to literature citations so that each time a work is mentioned the complete citation need not be looked up by refering to the original. (The various methods of citation are mentioned briefly in chapter 5 and in the *Style Manual for Biological Journals.*)

Manuals.—A *manual* is a document produced as a working tool compiled from existing literature with or without original information added to the existing scattered publications. Entomologists usually think of manuals as books dealing with the insects as a single order for a particular region. Many of these are listed in the bibliography of this book.

Textbooks.—Textbooks are particularly designed for instruction. These may include information about insects, methods for their study or control, and their nomenclature.

Reference works.—Reference works are a category of documents that has been considered in detail in chapter 7. There are various general books on insects that may be included here that would not be considered as search tools, as well as glossaries and encyclopedias (see bibliography).

*Current status series.—*These volumes are generally produced annually as a review and conceptualization of the recent literature reporting research on a single restricted topic. Several articles are written for each of the annual volumes, prepared by authors thought to be particularly knowledgeable in one of the topics, both selected in advance by the editors. Over a period of years most topics of a particular field are reviewed. Therefore, each article must cover several years of literature, not just that of the previous year.

Perhaps some of the most useful tools to appear in recent years are the several series of these current status reviews. This is reprocessed information at its best. We recognize that there is room for improvement in these, but in many ways they are far more valuable for the individual than the journals produced by societies.

One immediate improvement that should be made is the selection of more representative topics. Many topics may not be covered at all while others of more popular interest, at least to the editors, are covered in detail and frequently. A second improvement, as suggested by the SATCOM report, is a more objective coverage of the literature. The current procedure permits a very selective bibliography, the authors generally omitting the literature they consider inferior or erroneous. This, of course, gives a biased view that may result in useless duplication of effort in future research (see problems of synthesis above.)

*Catalogs.—*The most important tool of the taxonomist is the catalog of taxa. This is known to the information retrieval specialist as the taxonomic data file (see chapter 2). Catalogs are of many and varied kinds. They form a complex subject both in theory and in practice and space here does not permit more than a shallow survey of the topic.

This is a subject that is more properly one for a book on taxonomic methods (see Blackwelder, 1967, and Mayr, 1969).

Several kinds of catalogs of insect groups are available. These range from a simple checklist of species to the descriptive catalog that resembles a revision or monograph. The checklist contains only a list of the species of a particular area. The classification catalog lists all of the published names with reference to the original descriptions. This kind of catalog distinguishes between the valid (senior synonym) and the synonymous (junior synonym) names. The names of the various taxa are arranged according to their categories into a classification. The catalog also gives a brief indication of the distribution of the species. Most of the catalogs of the insects of North America are of this type. They may give, in addition to the above, an indication of the important revisions, references to identification keys, anatomical studies, and notes on the biology, including hosts.

Sometimes regional faunal studies are called catalogs, or descriptive catalogs. These are equivalent to the "floras" of the botanists.

FEATURES OF A GOOD CLASSIFICATION CATALOG

All species and infraspecific taxa listed and arranged by senior synonyms, with complete citations to original descriptions and the location of the type noted.

Citations for synonymizations, both generic and specific.

Type species of genera cited, including those improperly designated, and the method of designation.

Taxa arranged according to an acceptable classification scheme, giving citations to the arrangement followed (new classifications must be documented either in the catalog or elsewhere with citations given).

Indication of the geographical range covered, and citations to the source of the geographical distribution information.

The bibliographic scope of the catalog with references to search resources examined.

References to identification keys, useful revisions or reviews, and subsequent descriptions. If the list is selective an indication of the extent of the omissions should be given.

Biological notes.

The classification catalog usually begins as a collection of 3 x 5 cards prepared for use in the process of revising a group. Infrequently one or a group of taxonomists set out to write a catalog. Careful planning in advance is needed to prevent time consuming duplication of this tedious work. The file cards are prepared from an existing catalog, if any, as a start. This is updated by using *Zoological Record* and any more recent publication that may be available. As with any file card index, there should be kept with the collection a record card showing what publications have been cataloged, the contents and scope of the file, and a format card to explain the arrangement of the citation. Various colors may be used to indicate categories, synonyms, cross-references, and other kinds of information. However, the more complex the system, the more time consuming it becomes (see chapter 2).

A program for machine retrieval of information from a catalog is described in chapter 7. The catalog outlined above may be stored on punch cards and the data retrieved by means of code cards for any kind of information desired, including not only names, but dates, authors, biological and geographical information.

ASSIGNMENT 8

With the aid of the bibliography at the end of this textbook, do the following exercises. In answering 8.2 through 8.8 state the source of the information.

8.1 Where would you look for a listing of articles on the physiology of insects published before 1860?

8.2 Who edited and published T. W. Harris's correspondence? What was the year of publication?

8.3 Was anything published upon *Semiothisa granitata* in 1947?

8.4 Where can you find a bibliography of C. V. Riley's writings? How many titles are listed in conjunction with other authors; how many in which Riley was sole author?

8.5 You are interested in *Malacosoma pluviale* Dyar, the Western Tent Caterpillar. When did if first come to the notice of entomologists that this insect was extending its range eastward? What is the most recent record of this movement?

8.6 In what journal and year did J. H. Comstock publish on the "Colorado Potato Beetle in Manitoba"?

8.7 What did William D. Peck write on injurious insects of Massachusetts?

8.8 A. J. Lintner published a series of connected papers entitled "Entomological Contributions." How many were there? Where was each published? How many titles in each?

OPTIONAL INVESTIGATION

Give the proper form for entry of the names of the entomologists listed below. Give alternate forms from which to make reference. State the authorities consulted in ascertaining the full names and their vernacular forms.

M. S. Merian, 1647-1717	K. B. von Wattenwyl, Recent
A. L. M. le Peletier, 1770-1845	W. L. Distant, Recent
J. L. LeConte, 19th Century U.S.	W. T. M. Forbes, Recent
T. L. Casey, Recent	J. L. R. Agassiz, 19th Century
R. V. Chamberlin, Recent	Comte de Castelnau, 19th Century
C. T. Brues, Recent	
E. T. Cresson, Recent	Lord Rothschild, Recent
G. T. Bethune Baker, Recent	C. R. Osten Sacken, 19th Century
Lord Walsingham, Recent	

Visit the library and examine several catalogs of insects and note their features. Make a file card for each, tell what kind of catalog it is, and evaluate each in terms of the "features of a good catalog" list given on page 138 of this text, i.e., tell how well the catalog meets these requirements.

REVIEW CHECKLIST

1. Define the terms printed in italics in this chapter.
2. Why is reprocessing of information needed?
3. What are three of the problems encountered in the synthesis of data?
4. Why isn't there a world catalog of insect pests?
5. Name the major features of a revision.
6. Why are current status series becoming popular?
7. Describe the several types of catalogs.
8. What are the features of a good catalog?
9. For each of the following questions, give the type of literature in which you would expect to find the information asked for (literature types involved: reviews, revisions, monographs, bibliographies, catalogs, manuals, textbooks, reference works, current status series.) Select the one that best fits the case; several may apply in part.

A list of the described species of *Physorhinus.* Keys to the species of Hemiptera of Connecticut. A modern key to the species of the genus

Anthrax. The distribution in detail of *Odontita dorsalis.* Information on the mouthpart of Homoptera.

10. How would you find out what literature is available on a particular group of insects?
11. Where would you find serial publications listed and the subjects indicated?
12. Where can one find a list of abbreviations used for periodicals?
13. Where are "not-for-profit" publications listed? "For-profit" publications?
14. How would you find out about the life of a particular author? His bibliography?
15. What is used to locate a particular author's collection? His types of new species?
16. Cite one or more publications that tell what institutions have collections of insects.
17. What books or papers describe taxonomic methods? Control methods? Ecological methods? Other methods?
18. How would you find references to expeditions and collecting trips?
19. What are available as glossaries for entomology?

CHAPTER 10

POPULAR LITERATURE

Entomology, like ornithology and malacology, has always had enough interest from non-professional public to support some trade publications, especially those with less technical detail than that used by the professional. Many entomological pamphlets are specifically written to tell how to control insect pests. A variety of such literature is available, but much of it is of an ephemeral nature, and is, therefore, very difficult literature to list. I know of no attempt to include these references in any taxonomic catalog.

A curious situation exists in both taxonomic and economic entomology. There is a lack of interest in insects as a hobby and at the same time the science is plagued by amateurs. The problem is simple: amateur entomologists want to do professional work without the proper background and training, and relatively few of these persons are interested in the science as an avocation. For example, we have millions of people "controlling" insects as experts with no more background than comes from reading the labels on a can. Those who collect, sort, and identify insects also want to write descriptions of new species. It is true that much of our taxonomic knowledge has been provided in the past by "amatuers", and it is equally true that a large volume of our taxonomic literature is worthless. Even more serious, we are required by the "objectivity" of the Code to preserve and carefully index the inaccurate as well as the good information. As is pointed out in chapter 5, editors should understand the nature of taxonomic papers and help imporve the publication of the literature from anyone who submits a manuscript that apparently meets the ritual requirements of the Code, but lacks the depth necessary to make it a scientific contribution. Unfortunately, this situation is not confined to publications from amateurs.

POPULAR LITERATURE

Popular books on insects and their biology
Federal and State leaflets, circulars, and bulletins
Magazine articles
Newspaper articles
Museum bulletins of a non-technical nature

This may explain why we do not have more hobbysts, and consequently, more in the way of the type of popular literature available to those interested in ornithology and malacology. This great need for entomology has not been met simply because the initial inertia has not been overcome. Perhaps, with the ever increasing free time available for recreation, and the interest in camping, conservation, and pollution, the time will come when the professional can enjoy the benefits of popular interest without suffering too much from bungling by the amateur. Those professionals who scoff at this are encouraging further amateur interference by not helping to channel their interest into other studies, as for example, rearing, life history, and distribution—studies that they are better qualified to make.

The retrieval of each of the kinds of popular literature is by means of the reference works found in the reference section of the library. Further treatment of this kind of search resource is not included in this text.

ASSIGNMENT 9

9.1 Visit the library and note how popular literature is filed. Examine an example of each of the kinds listed in this chapter. Prepare a reference card for these.

OPTIONAL INVESTIGATION

Prepare a bibliography of popular literature on a subject of your choice. This should be useful to a non-professional who may write for information on the subject. The bibliography should include some recent magazine articles.

REVIEW CHECKLIST

1. What kinds of popular literature are available for entomology?
2. What are some of the problems in treating this information?
3. Why aren't more of these kinds of documents available?

CHAPTER 11

SOCIETIES, INSTITUTIONS, AND PERSONNEL

Jules Vernes once said that if three Americans became interested in a subject, they immediately elected a president, a secretary, and a treasurer, and a new society was born. There are many entomological societies in North America, and many institutions supporting entomological studies, teaching, research, and collections. Knowledge of these is often helpful in tracing down stored data of several kinds, such as files, manuscripts, and specimens.

Entomologists suffer not only by a lack of numbers but also by their extreme isolation from other branches of biology. This professional provincialism is not unique with this field to be sure, but it is inexcusable nevertheless. It would be advantageous for every entomolist if he thought of himself as a biologist specializing in the study of insects. The biological sciences, as the medical sciences, have many specialities, but the members of the latter profession maintain their identity with the general public. The fractionation of biological science practioners so dilutes this group of professionals that their image to the public is barely noticeable. As for entomologists, they more often are known to the public as odd fellows with insect nets or as killers of wildlife and polluters of the environment. We would find it beneficial to join forces with other biologists and direct some attention toward good public relations.

INSTITUTIONAL INFORMATION SOURCES

Entomological societies
Universities offering a program in entomology
Field stations
Museums and collections
Federal and state experiment stations
Pesticide industry
Pest control industry
National and state parks, forests, and preserves
Entomological equipment and supply houses
Book publishers and antiquarian bookmen

Entomological societies.—Most societies are identified by the publications they produce. All major countries of the world have a national entomological society. In the United States the *Entomological Society of America* is the professional society. This is probably the largest society with over 6,000 members. The membership lists of this and other societies provide us with a roster of those interested in this science. My estimate of the number of persons in the world considered to be professional entomologists is only 40,000. In terms of other branches of science this is very small. For example, the *World Almanac* lists 40,000 members in 1968 for the *Geological Institute of America.* (In the same Almanac no entomological society is listed). The *American Forestry Association* lists many more members in America than there are entomologists in the world.

The entomological societies are the principal source for biographical information, bibliographies, and history of the science. But there is no systematic attempt to report this kind of information. Usually the data concerning entomologists are reported by surviving friends who are in a position to publish and buy a stock of reprints. Histories seem to be forgotten.

Regional, national, and international society meetings serve as an excellent communication media, but only for a select few. This is the most costly and the most haphazard form of scientific communication. Papers are presented, but have a restricted audience. They are usually rather poorly prepared and poorly delivered. Taxonomic papers seldom generate any interest. (These could be improved if authors would remember to show a progression of characteristics instead of attempting to deliver an oral catalog of species.) Most of those in attendance feel that any worthwhile paper will be published, so little attention is paid to the data details presented. These might as well be omitted. The real value of the meeting comes from the first hand association with people of similar interests. This should be recognized by administrators. Once they remove the necessity of presenting a paper at a meeting in order for an employee to merit travel funds, attention can be directed toward improving meetings as a form of information retrieval. As it is now, the retrieval efficiency is very low. Personalities are often involved which result in the creation of "cliques" or similar groups of rather smug scientists. The ecology of most meetings is nearly as complex as that of the insects under study! Nonetheless, for those who attend these sessions they are very rewarding. Serious study is being given to their continued improvement.

Because of the concentration of societies on the production of original documents, only slight attention is given to informal information exchange which is greatly needed. In particular, societies could do more to coordinate research projects (see also chapter 2, Information Service Centers, and SATCOM recommendations C1, C14, and E7). At the present time, the only source for project announcements other than the Science Information Exchange (p. 115) is the back cover of such publications as *Entomological News* and the *Coleopterists' Bulletin* (see also the bibliography).

Universities offering a program in entomology.–The same lack of coordination exists among university departments of entomology as among societies. They are unnoticed by most students outside of the department and many other biological science departments on other campuses. The only directory of biological science departments omits at least 6 major entomology departments in major universities of the United States because their existence was unknown to the compilers. The separation of entomology departments from the rest of the biological sciences is seriously debated by many. This is not to say that the specialized training in the science is questioned.

Information exchange between entomology departments is virtually nonexistent. Classes are conducted but only the enrolled students benefit from the ideas and methods presented in these classes because of the lack of a general curriculum exchange. Seminars are organized and presented, but the ideas circulated find their way to only a few. Even invited speakers find limited audiences. Provision for wider circulation of this kind of information is needed. University information networks, such as the Interuniversity Communications Council (EDUCOM) are working to improve this situation.

Field stations.—A great variety of summer field stations are maintained in North America, but none are particularly devoted to entomology. No complete directory of these institutions exists.

Museums and private collections.—Taxonomists depend heavily upon insect collections as a source of data for their research. Only one attempt has been made to list the collections in North America (see bibliography) and this only for the Coleoptera. These guides are needed for other groups. They should include information about the collection, its special groups, types, loan rules, expeditions, and publications.

Federal and state experiment stations.—The network of agricultural experiment stations supporting entomological services and research is very extensive and provides the major support for the science. Information networks are being formed for the circulation of information among these employees. A directory of personnel, project descriptions, and project reports are available. It is likely that the distribution of this information will be fully automated in the near future as a part of the Current Research Information System (CRIS).

Pesticide industry.—Several large corporations and a variety of diversified industries are concerned with research on insect control as well as the manufacture and packaging of pesticides. These concerns employ a significant proportion of professional entomologists. Circulation of information throughout the field is limited, but some kinds of reports are available for general use although they are not widely announced and they are not well cataloged.

Pest control industry.—The public is most conscious of the entomological profession through its contact with pest control operators (sometimes called exterminators). Although the industry has been slow to achieve professional standards the post World War II years have been active ones in the development of the field. Purdue University's annual Pest Control Operator's Conference (PCO), and its correspondence course for PCO's are among the most active programs for this branch of entomology. Several excellent manuals have been produced for use by the profession (see bibliography) and specialized trade journals exist. No information centers have been established as yet, but an EDP information service most certainly would be of great use to this group.

National and State parks, forests, and preserves.—The preservation of natural areas and the description of the flora and fauna of these areas will be a major project for the next decades. There is no comprehensive list of these regions but some groups have made preliminary, state-wide studies (see bibliography). More needs to be done, perhaps by setting up a central coordination center by interested agencies and societies in all branches of biology.

Entomological equipment and supply houses.—Several firms supplying biological equipment and specimens have special divisions for entomology and a few specialize in entomology. The low volume demand for these materials makes them costly and generally of secondary interest to these business concerns. A list of the major suppliers is given in Appendix III because this is a source of entomological information also.

Book publishers and antiquarian bookmen.—Commercially produced professional books and textbooks are published by a number of companies. Used and out-of-print entomological literature may be obtained from a few of the large book dealers. Their current, and also their past catalogs are interesting and sometimes important bibliographical references. These dealers are listed in Appendix II of this book.

DIRECTORY OF ENTOMOLOGISTS

A directory of entomologists and entomological departments, societies, and establishments of the world is nonexistent, but if one were available it would be extremely useful. Such a directory could be produced and be up-dated annually. Probably the best way to provide this service is by means of an EDP information center. The directory should list all of the institutions and organizations discussed in this chapter, with cross indexing by personnel and field of interest. An annual print-out could be provided if each of the societies and organizations gave it their support. Current listings by subject using EDP equipment would provide governmental, educational, and industrial agencies with a much needed service. Although no service of this kind was specificially recommended by the SATCOM report, it was implied, and it would seem to be of concern to the Information Retrieval Committee of the Entomological Society of America.

ASSIGNMENT 10

10.1 List 10 major insect collections from which you might borrow specimens of Elateridae.

10.2 If you wished to do research on Noctuidae, where is an appropriate graduate school you might attend?

10.3 Who manufactures the genuine Schmitt box?

10.4 How would you get permission to collect insects in a national park?

10.5 How can you find out the location of the Walter Horn types?

OPTIONAL INVESTIGATION

Select a group of insects of interest to you and compile a list of people in North America interested in the same group. Give references to your source of this information. Compose a letter that you might send to borrow specimens for study; do the same for the return of specimens.

REVIEW CHECKLIST

1. List some advantages and some disadvantages of having a large number of entomological societies.
2. What are the limitations of society meetings?
3. How many universities have departments of entomology in the United States and Canada? How many professors of entomology?
4. What is the relationship of balance between commercial, governmental, and educational organizations and professional entomology?
5. Give some examples of the following: national parks; state parks; forests; reservations; private preserves. How might you find out where there are others?
6. Where can you purchase the following items: insect pins; insect boxes; insect specimens; a textbook of entomology; a publication written by Thomas L. Casey?

GLOSSARY

The terms defined in this glossary are placed in italic type when first mentioned or used in the text. The page number at the end of the definition refers to the location of the term in the text.

abbreviation a shortened word or phrase, often a random contraction, used to save space, but may be misleading or ambiguous; see standard list of abbreviations given in the *Style Manual for Biological Journals.* [p. 69]

abstract a summary of facts included in the body of a book or paper; not over 3% of the text; not a description of contents but the information itself (if an informative abstract); a tool for keeping abreast with the current literature. [p. 8]

acronym a word formed from the initial letters or groups of letters of words in a phrase or title. [p. 114]

ADP Automatic data processing (see also EDP). [p. 8]

analysis of subject content (see information coding). [p. 19]

annals a periodical containing records of discoveries, transactions of a society, and similar records. [p. 75]

annotation a single sentence or single paragraph indicative abstract. [p. 87]

author's alteration usually any change made after the printer sets the originally submitted copy into type, which includes changes in standing matter (*q.v.*) made by the editor. These changes are more costly per line than the original typesetting because old lines have to be removed and new lines added to the galleys, then new proofs taken, all of which is time consuming. This is one of the most misunderstood aspects of printing. [p. 71]

automatic data processing (ADP) the handling of data by means of machines. [p. 8]

balanced page printing, as one of the fine arts, should be pleasing to the eye through a balance of the elements of a printed page. This is achieved by the proper placing of illustrations on the page, by equal page length for opposing pages, by breaking paragraphs only after the second line from the top, down to the second line from the bottom, by the proper use of headings and subheadings, and by the balanced use of type so that it is not "busy". A balanced page is of concern to an author only in that he should leave the type size and styles to the editor and closely follow the format of the magazine in which he hopes to publish. Underlining, capitalizing, and similar typographic indications should be left to the editor to mark for the printer. [p. 74]

bibliography a list of authors, titles, and references to information documents. [p. 115, 136]

binary digits a system of numerical notation to the base two, in which each place of a number, expressed either as 0 or 1, corresponds to a power of 2. [p. 10]

binding the securing of pages and signatures into a unit as in a magazine, pamphlet, or book. Many kinds of bindings are available including side stitched (staples through the sides of the folded pages), saddle stitched (staples through the fold (end) of the sheets), perfect binding (glue holding edges of cut sheets) or sewn binding (as used in books with a glued cover, usually with headbands (the colorful strip of cloth reinforcement at the top edge of the binding used so the cloth of the binding will not tear when the book is pulled from the shelf by placing a finger on this top edge)). [p. 77]

bit see binary digit. [p. 10]

blue pencil a pencil used by editors for instructions to printers;

blue will not reproduce when used on drawings and other material to be photographed for cuts or offset plates. [p. 74]

boldface   heavy, dark letters of the same size and type face as Roman type. [The word "boldface" in the above line is set in boldface type; p. 74]

bulletin   a periodical publication containing the proceedings of a society. [p. 75]

caps   the upper case (top of the type box) or capital letters in a font of type (see lower case). [p. 74]

characters   the letters, punctuation, numerals, and spaces in a line or other unit of printing. [p. 68]

class numbers   the notation used as a shorthand reference in the classification schedule. [p. 87]

classification schedule   a listing of index or subject headings arranged in a generic and specific classification to bring like terms together. [p. 95]

coated paper   (see glossy paper.) [p. 70]

code term   a term under which entries are made in the index. [p. 13, 84]

coden   a short form abbreviation of the title of a periodical. [p. 114]

colophon   a notice placed at the end of a pamphlet or book with information about typefaces, paper, and binding. [p. 78]

composing   the act of setting the typescript (or copy, *q.v.*) into type after it is marked (or edited, *q.v.*) by the editor. [p. 77]

composition   that which is composed (see composing). [p. 74]

computer   a machine, usually electronic, used to carry out complex mathematical operations at high speed. [p. 1]

conceptual analysis   the matching of the subject content analysis with the terms used in the thesaurus or index. [p. 95]

contribution   a series of writings for publication, especially a periodical. [p. 75]

controlled vocabulary   a list of subjects as class labels to be used in arranging or grouping documents. [p. 90]

core journal a journal dealing with a single discipline, devoting 85 to 90% of its space to the special subject. [p. 19]

corrections (see proof reading). [p. 74]

copy the typescript (improperly called manuscript, *q.v.*) and illustrations used by the compositors in setting type and making engravings, or otherwise producing forms for printing. [p. 74]

copyright a certificate issued by the Library of Congress, upon application and the deposit of two copies of the published (i.e., printed) material, showing the date of deposit to help establish publication rights and ownership. [p. 70]

critical abstract an abstract that reviews a document. [p. 124]

current awareness an output product for informing the user of currently produced literature. [p. 4]

current status publication reviews of research developments issued in book form under a general editorship, but written by leading authorities on the particular topics. [p. 53]

data facts or statistics, either historical or derived from calculations or experimentation. [p. 1]

data documents stored data indexed and made available for use but not published for mass distribution. [p. 46]

data retrieval system (DRS) a search or look-up system for facts. [p. 7]

date of publication the actual date a publication is placed on sale, usually indicated by the date the publication was first mailed to subscribers. In the case of periodicals with a second class mailing permit (*q.v.*), the records of the mailing are kept by the post office. Librarians stamp the date of receipt of a publication as a record of the publication date. These actual dates of availability frequently differ considerably from the date printed on the publication. [p. 102]

deletion something removed from the proof either as a typographical error or as an author's alteration (*q.v.*). [p. 74]

descriptor words used to list the contents of a document (see code term). [p. 8]

discipline oriented a project concerned with a specialized subject. [p. 18]

disk pack a random access data cell composed of a set of rotating metal disks. [p. 38]

document any written item, as a book, article, letter, note file, etc., of a factual or informative nature communicated or stored. [p. 2]

document profile the code or index of a document. [p. 89]

double space the separation of all lines of a typescript by a space equal to the space occupied by the line of type. [p. 69]

DRS see data retrieval system. [p. 7]

duplication any form of reproduction of printed matter by whatever process that provides one or more exact copies. In order for duplicated copies to be considered published, they must be reproduced by a process that reasonably prohibits alteration so that the copies reproduced are all exact copies. Generally the process involved uses a permanent "ink" as opposed to a photographic process or a "spirit" process. The ink need not be fluid; e.g., "toner" used in xerography is a powdered ink. [p. 57]

editing a process of handling typescripts for publication which includes checking format, suggesting additions, deletions, rewording, checking illustrations, and the marking of copy for the printer (see editor). [p. 74]

editor a person who prepares typescript for a printer and otherwise handles the copy and format of a publication (see also managing editor). [p. 65]

editorial board a small group of individuals, usually appointed rather than elected (in the case of a society publication) who review typescripts, at least those questioned by the editor, and make recommendations to the editor regarding the acceptability of a typescript for publication in the particular journal, the format of a publication, and matters of editorial policy (*q.v.*). When papers are turned down for publication, an editor has less explaining to do if he can say that the editorial board, as an abstract being, turned it down. [p. 75]

editorial liberty to interject the personal opinion of the editor, or to proceed in a manner opposed to editorial policy (*q.v.*). [p. 74]

editorial policy the rules laid down by the editor and/or editorial board to guide in adjusting format and selecting articles for publication. [p. 69]

EDP see Electronic data processing. [p. 4]

electronic data processing (EDP) the handling of data by electronic equipment. [p. 8]

ferric tape a roll of plastic coated with an iron compound used to electronically store information of many kinds including punch card records, sound and photograph recordings and machine gathered data. [p. 39]

figure a single illustration, either line cut or halftone, inserted into the text or grouped with other figures to form a plate (*q.v.*). [p. 70]

file card a card, which may be of various standard sizes and colors, used to store and retrieve coded references and data. [p. 32]

flowchart a diagram or chart showing the steps needed for a process. [p. 14]

font of type the complete set of individual pieces of type including all letters, signs, symbols, and spaces used in the composition of a typescript set into type. [p. 74]

footnote a means of publishing documentary information or comment that otherwise, if included in the text, detracts from the main thought of a sentence or paragraph; expensive to set into type and should be avoided whenever possible. [p. 69]

format the design and style of a publication, including contents, arrangement, and printing details. [p. 66]

foundry type printing type cast as individual characters for hand setting as opposed to machine set type, i.e., movable type. [p. 74]

galley proof type set from copy is stored in long metal racks (galleys) holding about three pages of printed matter, from which four or more long sheets or "proof" are printed and submitted to editors for correction. One set is for the author, one for the editor's file, one for the editor to mark his and the author's corrections and returned to the printer, and one, usually on colored stock, to mark for the arrangement of the pages. [p. 71]

gazette a newspaper. [p. 75]

glossy paper paper with a smooth, shiny finish used particularly for the letterpress (*q.v.*) printing of detailed halftones; the paper used by "slick" magazines. Some glossy paper is coated after the manufacture of the paper base and is then referred to as coated paper. [p. 70]

halftone an illustration composed of fine dots due to a screening process, made from a photograph or detailed drawing using shades and tones, used for printing these pictures as opposed to a line cut (*q.v.*). The fineness of the screen used determines the detail possible in the halftone. Editors usually indicate the screen they desire, as 110, 120, etc., indicating the number of dots per inch. [p. 70]

hanging indentation a reversed paragraph so that the first few letters of the first word or words project to the left of the following lines of the paragraph. An arrangement of type that falls short of the fixed right or left hand margin of the page. Indented matter is more costly than "straight set", i.e., paragraph arranged copy, and authors should avoid this format. [p. 69]

illustration figure or plate made from a drawing or photograph prepared by a separate process to form a printing block inserted into the page of type and printed with the type. [p. 70]

imprint the printer's or publisher's name as it appears on a book or magazine to identify the source of the publication. [p. 78]

indentation (see hanging indentation and paragraph indentation.) [p. 69]

index a set of code terms under which entries (or references) are made. [p. 71]

index language the complete set of terms used in indexing or coding to describe document content including rules for use, subheadings, and order of reference for compound terms. [p. 90]

index terms unique definitions of the document class, i.e., index terms identify and classify a document. [p. 96]

indexing system of data retrieval generally used in a book; seldom possible to achieve 100% retrieval unless skillfully done (see machine indexing). [p. 84]

indicative abstract an abstract (*q.v.*) that describes the original document but does not contain data itself. [p. 124]

information the contents of documents available concerning particular facts or circumstances. [p. 1]

information bank the stored and coded information source. [p. 8]

information center the location of the information bank and the IRS (*q.v.*). [p. 8]

information coding a process of identification of a document or record and noting contents through code terms or index terms. [p. 19, 89]

information retrieval system (IRS) a search system for documents; a reference search system informing users of the whereabouts of documents relating to the request. [p. 8]

informative abstract an abstract (*q.v.*) that summarizes the major facts, ideas, and conclusions of a document. [p. 124]

input the data or materials introduced into a system. [p. 14]

IRS (see information retrieval system). [p. 8]

italics letters of type that are curved and slanted to resemble writing, used primarily for foreign words in a publication; sometimes used for emphasis. [*This is italic type*; p. 74]

journal a periodical publication. [p. 75]

justified right hand margin an arrangement of type set with variable spacing so that the last word of each line reaches the right hand margin to form a straight line, as opposed to the irregular right hand margin of an ordinary typewritten page. [p. 77]

key sort cards file cards of various sizes and forms with a series of marginal holes used as a means of coding and for retrieval. [p. 34]

key words the same as descriptors (*q.v.*). [p. 8]

key words in context (KWIC) a system of title coding by machine using words in the title of a record. [p. 97]

key words out of context (KWOC) a system of title coding by machine using an enriched title of a record. [p. 97]

killed type a portion of set type not used; it is "killed" by removing from the galley rack and melting or distributing back into the type trays if it is foundry type. [p. 75]

KWIC (see key words in context). [p. 97]

KWOC (see key words out of context.) [p. 97]

leads narrow strips of metal less than type height, cut to the line measure (*q.v.*) and of 1 or 2 points (*q.v.*) in thickness, used to separate lines of type. [p. 74]

letterpress a printing process involving moveable type, including foundry, linotype, or monotype and cuts, inked by rollers and impressed directly upon the paper. [p. 76]

line cut a drawing using simple lines with only lines or dots for shading, converted into a block for printing, and suitable for either glossy paper or a paper with a rougher finish. [p. 70]

line measure the width of a page of type in picas, hence the full width of a linotype slug even if the type is indented. [p. 74]

linotype a machine that sets type, with a keyboard, using molds arranged into a line and casts from this line of molds (or matrices) to form a line of lead alloy type, called a linotype slug. These slugs are arranged into a galley of type. A font of matrices is placed on the machine, usually consisting of the following combination of any one size and face of type: Roman, italic, and small caps, or Roman, italic, and boldface. Some type faces may be mixed on the machine, but this is more expensive composition, as is also the setting of special characters not on the keyboard, e.g., sex signs. [p. 77]

literature information in printed form and distributed to libraries and individuals. [p. 2]

lower case the non-capital letters in a type face, so named because they are kept in the front part (or lower part of an inclined case) of the case or tray containing foundry type. [p. 74]

machine indexing a programmed method of scanning a document for key words for indexing using EDP equipment. [p. 97]

magazine a periodical containing miscellaneous articles, stories, poems, etc. [p. 75]

magnetic core an iron network capable of retaining magnetic charges representing binary digits (bits) and used as the memory bank of a computer. [p. 1, 38]

make ready the preparation of the press for printing, which includes the inking of the press, the adjustment of the type or plates, and the adjustment of the paper and paper feed. If a chase (the frame holding the type) is removed from the press and replaced for the printing of an additional run or the printing of reprints, the press has to be made ready again with additional charges added to the bill from the printer. [p. 78]

managing editor an editor who transacts business with authors and printers for publication; may be synonymous with editor. [p. 76]

manual a publication, usually a book, of a useful nature, generally with instructions or a tool for identification. [p. 136]

manuscript (see typescript); the hand written original of the publication used as printer's copy (no longer accepted by printers). [p. 31]

marking for printer the indications of type size, style, line length, and spacing to be followed by the printer in composing the article. [p. 74]

memoir a record of investigations of any subject. [p. 136]

microcard a print from microfilm or microfiche. [p. 34]

microfiche a sheet of microfilm in a form suitable for filing, containing a series of separate negatives reduced in size and photographically printed on transparent stock. [p. 34]

microfilm a photograph record of a document which greatly reduces the page size and thereby reduces the storage space needed for the record. [p. 34]

mission oriented a project designed to reach a particular goal, e.g., control of an insect, rather than a particular subject (see discipline oriented). [p. 18]

monograph a special trestise on a particular subject; a work including many data not of an original nature (therefore, synthesized information) as a complete review of a specific topic. [p. 47]

monotype machine set and cast type, but using single characters the same as foundry type, as opposed to a line of type cast at one time. Errors may be individually corrected instead of recasting the entire line; also, pages may be remotely set using paper tape for casting instructions. [p. 77]

notation a code listing for the classification schedule as a shorthand reference, each one referred to as class numbers (*q.v.*). [p. 96]

notations in margins   editorial notations for the printer or the author; the reason for wide margins on all sides and for double spacing of typescripts. [p. 69]

notebook   a filing system similar to a card system, but with loose leaves (i.e., paper may be inserted, removed, or the position changed, sorted) or bound, rendering more portability to the system. [p. 33]

offset   a printing process involving a special plate, usually prepared photographically, placed on a drum and inked. The ink is transferred to a second drum and this is passed over the printing paper, resulting in a positive image on the paper. Offset printing is used for typewriter composed articles and in long production runs of plates made from regular type composition. Its chief advantages are the cost cutting possibilities as a result of the typewriter composition and some saving in the cost of illustrations. [p. 77]

optical coincidence system   a retrieval system using a punched sheet as a reference to numbered and coded documents; light passed through sheets show, by reading coordinates, the number of the document containing the requested information. [p. 37]

orientation card   a card used to show the purpose of a file system and the source of information actually included. [p. 32]

original document   the first recorded results of direct observation or experimentation, or record of events, when published, or otherwise made available to any interested person. [p. 39]

output   the information, document, data, or product of a system. [p. 14]

overmatter   type left standing after the make-up of an issue of a periodical which will be used in a succeeding issue, or killed (see standing matter). [p. 75]

page   one side of a sheet of paper used in a magazine, book or pamphlet. [p. 77]

page proof   printer's proof of the type after it is made up into pages, but before it is placed on the press for printing. Page proof is generally sent only to the editor. Occassionally a publisher supplies authors with page proof only for final checking, the publisher having assumed the responsibility for the corrections of the galley proof. Offset page proof is called "blue-line" or VanDyke proof and is produced photographically from the offset negatives used to make the final plates. [p. 75]

paper printing may be done on almost any kind of paper, but certain finishes are better than others, e.g., glossy finish paper for half-tones, book paper for text; other finishes include English, laid, cover paper, etc. Paper weights are determined according to a ream (of 500 sheets) in the sizes used by printers. This is also referred to as the "substance" and indirectly indicates the thickness of the paper. [p. 76]

paper tape a machine produced record stored on a roll of paper used for recovery on automatic equipment to reproduce the record. [p. 38]

paragraph indentation an indication of the beginning of a paragraph by the indentation of the first line approximately 1 to 3 quads, or squares of type. Typescripts should always indicate paragraphs by indentation to save the editor the necessity of marking each paragraph. The modern "block" style must be avoided in typescript preparation, unless each paragraph is separated, when printed, by a blank space. [p. 69]

periodical a publication issued at regular intervals for an indefinite period of time. [p. 48]

peripheral literature all publications not considered core literature, i.e., literature in sources not primarily devoted to the subject or topic of interest to the user. [p. 47]

permutation of terms progressive changes of the order of terms. The number of entries needed is $2^{(n-1)}$ where n=number of elements in the document's subject designation. [p. 97]

PERT acronym for "program evaluation review technique". [p. 15]

picas a unit of measure used in printing and publishing. A pica is 1/6 of an inch. [p. 74]

plates a collection of figures (*q.v.*) grouped together for a single page, or part of a page. [p. 70]

point a unit of measure used to indicate the size (height) of type; 1 point equals about 1/72nd of an inch. [p. 74]

printer the person or firm that actually prints the publication (see also, publisher). [p. 75]

printer's devil   a printer's helper who is learning the trade; an experience that would help authors and editors to understand printer's bills and h..p them to keep down printing expenses. [p. 73]

printing   a form of duplicating records by the use of paper and ink; usually refers to material set in type. [p. 2]

proceedings   minutes of a society, etc. [p. 75]

proof   (see galley proof, page proof, or revised proof.) Single copies, printed by a special proof press on one side of a sheet to be used for corrections before the publication is printed on the regular press. [p. 71]

proof reading   the checking of galley proof (*q.v.*) for errors in typesetting.   Errors and corrections are indicated by using a standard set of marks (usually these marks are given in a dictionary or in books on writing).   Generally only galley proof is sent to authors; page proof is checked by the editor who makes certain that linotype corrections are made without introducing new errors.   Sometimes it is necessary to reset more than a single line because of the length of the correction in one line involves the next line and so on to the end of the paragraph. The additional lines need to be checked as well.   The printer often marks these on the revised proof.   [p. 71]

proportional spacing   type with a proportional size according to that needed by the letter rather than a fixed space for each letter as on most typewriters.   Ordinary printing type is proportionally spaced and some typewriters have proportional spacing.   [p. 77]

publication   that which is published, usually by printing, but includes other forms of duplication of records.   [p. 2, 48]

publisher   the person or firm that handles the production of the publication, but seldom is the printer of the work, i.e., publishers usually are not printers; instead they contract with a print shop for the printing. Thus, even though a publisher may be known as a "Press" there are no presses in the establishment. [p. 65, 75]

punch cards   a standard size and form of card used for ADP in an IRS. [p. 37]

queries   editors and printers question words or omissions in typescripts by marking the spot on a galley proof with a question mark. This is used also to indicate the need for a page number or similar information obtainable only after a further step in the printing process. [p. 71]

random access data cell a version of the iron core system of information storage permitting a greater versitility of storage and retrieval through a random storage process (see also disk pack). [p. 38]

record any durable packet of information used in the communication of facts. [p. 2]

reference a notation that indicates the location of a record; a key to the location of a fact or datum; the location of source materials. [p. 20]

reference work a volume or set of books used to recover information as opposed to sequencial reading. [p. 136]

rejected paper typescript returned as unacceptable to the editor and/or editorial board or reviewers either because it is inappropriate for the publication, or because it does not meet the standards set for the publication. [p. 73]

reprints a tradition among authors of having copies of their articles printed separately after the original printing of the publication, with any extraneous matter removed from the first and last page of the article, and with the insertion of a notation as to the place of publication of the original. Reprints are costly and time consuming because of the need to reink and make-ready the press for several such articles usually in runs of 100 to 200. These are circulated among the few that are interested in the article, often the only ones that are interested, and this in turn cuts down on the circulation of the publication (see also separates and tear sheets). The system may be replaced soon by xerography and Data Documents. [p. 75]

request profile the results of the analysis and coding of the search request. [p. 89]

retrospective search an output product enabling a search through past literature. [p. 20]

reversed plate a printing plate made as a negative rather than a positive so that the background rather than the letters print, leaving the letters white in contrast to the background color. [p. 77]

review a periodical containing primarily critical articles; also a summary of the data on a taxon. [p. 46, 75, 133]

reviewers a group of specialists usually picked by editors and assumed to be, and usually are, well enough versed in a field to render expert judgement of the merits of a typescript to help the editor in his chore of selecting suitable articles for publication. [p. 70]

revised proof proof of the reset corrected galley of an originally bad proof; called for by the editor when substantial changes are made in the galley proof stage. [p. 74]

revision a new classification of a taxon; also a new version of a typescript of an article. [p. 47, 134]

screen a measure of dots used in halftone plate making. [p. 74]

search file the store of codes used as the reference or "look-up" for documents; the bibliography. [p. 19]

search profile (see request profile). [p. 89]

search request the question posed to an IRS which is processed to retrieve a document. [p. 18]

search resources publications, catalogs, files, and indexes used to locate documents and records. [p. 110]

second class mailing permit a special permit secured from the Post Office Department for the mailing of periodicals. Special fees and special mailing procedures are required. This is used by publications because of the reduced rates of postage. [p. 78]

secondary literature information reviewed or otherwise synthesized from original documents and republished or made available to any interested person. [p. 39]

selective dissemination of information (SDI) matching user interests with document profiles; similar to Data Documents (*q.v.*). [p. 56]

separates some periodicals issue each article as a separate publication mailed at irregular intervals as they become available from the printer. These are then gathered into numbers and volumes. This is a system that should be used by those desiring reprints for private circulation, but a system most suitable for longer (32 pages or more) article (see also reprints and tear sheets). [p. 78]

serial a publication issued at irregular intervals for a definite period of time or until a definite objective is reached. [p. 46]

series   a set of volumes or parts issued successively having some close connection as a set.   [p. 47]

sheet   a piece of paper forming the leaf of a publication, usually printed on both sides, and therefore representing 2 pages; also a term used to refer to an unfolded signature (*q.v.*).   [p. 77]

signature   a large sheet of paper upon which are printed, on both sides, several pages of a publication, which is then folded to form pages in units of 4, 8, 12, 16, 32, 36, or rarely more pages. Signatures are gathered and bound to form a magazine or book.   [p. 77]

source documents   the records suitable for storage utilizing EDP equipment.   [p. 2]

small caps   capital letters of the same height as lower case (*q.v.*) letters usually used for emphasis or to set apart an item. They may be used in combination with caps, but never with lower case or italics.   [p. 74]

spaces   the spaces that separate letters, numbers, or lines, either as blank pieces of type of various sizes, or as leads (*q.v.*).   [p. 74]

special fourth class rate   a reduced postal rate for typescripts, books, and other academic materials.   [p. 74]

standing matter   type set which is reused in each issue (see also overmatter).   [p. 75]

stored information   any knowledge placed on record for the use of one or more persons.   [p. 27]

subject headings   the individual index terms arranged alphabetically in a controlled vocabulary (*q.v.*).   [p. 96]

subject index   a classification process for elementary subjects using the controlled vocabulary.   [p. 96]

synthesized information   secondary literature presenting data in a condensed and coordinated form.   [p. 19]

system design   a procedure or logical plan outlining major steps of a process with descriptions of each detail so that each stage is coordinated and efficient.   [p. 14]

taxonomic data file   a file of names and references to records pertaining to organisms; generally called a "catalog".   [p. 20]

tear sheets pages torn from an issue used to circulate as reprints (*q.v.*). Often times the purchase of additional copies of a publication is cheaper than the purchase of reprints (see also separates and reprints). [p. 78]

terminal a direct connection, by teletype keyboard, with a computer system. [p. 38]

textbook a book used as a special source of information particularly as an introduction to a subject with instructions for learning the subject. [p. 137]

thesaurus a dictionary or index of synonyms and antonyms useful for conceptual analysis. [p. 20]

tip-in an illustration printed separately either on different paper (e.g., glossy paper when the text is on non-glossy paper), oversized and folded sheets (as a map for example), or for artistic purposes, and pasted separately into the issue. [p. 70]

transaction the record of activities, addresses, etc., of meetings. [p. 75]

treatise a systematic exposition or argument in writing; a methodical discussion of the facts and principles involved and conclusions reached. [p. 136]

type the embossed unit representing letters and other characters, including spaces of various sizes used for printing. Foundary type, monotype, and linotype slugs are cast at a standard and accurate height for an even impression on the printing paper. Foundry type is notched to show the case and position of the embossing on the body. [p. 74]

type face the style of the type as a design; type styling is an art dating back to the time of the invention of movable type in the 16th century. Many of our familiar type faces have come to us from these early artists. Careful study of type will show the artistic qualities of each of the many hundreds of kinds. The colophon (*q.v.*) of those good books that have one, identifies the type face and often gives a brief history of the face. [p. 74]

typescript a typewritten article used as copy by the editor and printer; a better term now than manuscript. [p. 31]

typewriter composition copy prepared on a typewriter, usually with proportional spacing (*q.v.*) and single spaced for use in the offset production of a magazine or book; usually the right hand margin is unjustified but machines such as the Varityper or the IBM Magnetic Tape Selectric Typewriter are available which permit justified right hand margins (*q.v.*). [p. 77]

underlining indicates a Latin (scientific) name or other foreign word in a typescript and tells the printer to set it in italic type. This is often useful for other text material, but can be carried to absurdity when used in titles, ordinary text, etc.; caps and/or small caps (*q.v.*) are usually more appropriate for all but specific names of insects in Latin. Such decisions should be left to the editor. [p. 69]

volume a complete unit of publication, either as a book, or as a number of issues of a magazine published over a fixed period of time with a stated frequency (usually the issues of one year). [p. 76]

work a volume on a single subject. [p. 72]

writing any written or printed document (*q.v.*). [p. 27]

xerography a process of duplication involving a source of light, a lens, an electrostatic charge, and heat as a fuser. A process that may be destined to revolutionize publishing, data storage, dissemination, and the used book market. [p. 32]

yearly subscription fee a publication charge that is frequently increased due to increased printing costs and lack of increased circulation. Advanced subscriptions enable a publisher to judge the production run of a publication which in turn determines the price because the more copies that are printed, the cheaper each unit costs. [p. 78]

zip code a necessary part of an author's address and should be included with his address citation printed with each article in a publication so that readers may more easily contact authors; a system to facilitate the delivery of United States mail. [p. 80]

BIBLIOGRAPHY OF BASIC TYPES OF ENTOMOLOGICAL LITERATURE

The works listed here are some examples of the entomological literature discussed in the text, as illustrations, or as additional references to supplement the text. All references cited in the text will be found in this section. This list is in no way exhaustive, but rather, it is meant to serve as a sampling of the vast literature resources for entomology. Certain works, for example, reference work, glossaries, and bibliographic collections should be examined in detail. It is useful to spend some time noting the organization and contents of each of the cited papers and volumes. In this manner the advantages and limitations of these can be seen.

Recent literature is favored, since the older literature, especially the taxonomic literature, may be found readily in the bibliographies of the standard volumes. The arrangement of the lists follows the order of discussion in the text. To locate a particular reference by author, refer to the author index at the end of the volume.

Chapter 1. The Information Problem

Arnett, R. H., Jr. 1966. Observation and experimentation. Systematic Zool., 15: 351-353.

Arnett, R. H., Jr. 1970. Data Documents. Ent. News, 81: 1-11.

Chapter 2. Information retrieval theory

Arnett, R. H., Jr. 1967b. Pilot laboratory: a center for the study of insect populations. Purdue University, 21 pp.

Bean, James L. 1964. A proposed system for electronic data processing of forest insect and disease survey information. United States Forest Serv., 32 pp.

Becker, Joseph and Robert M. Hayes. 1963. Information storage and retrieval: tools, elements, theories. John Wiley and Sons, N.Y., xi+ 448 pp.

Bourne, Charles P. 1963. Methods of information handling. John Wiley and Sons, N. Y., xiv + 241 pp.

Brown, W. S., J. R. Pierce, and J. F. Traub. 1967. The future of scientific journals. Science, 158: 1153-1159.

Council on Biological Sciences Information. 1970. Information handling in the life sciences. National Research Council, Washington, D. C., [x] + 79 pp.

Foote, Richard H. *et al.* 1968. Report of the special committee on retrieval of scientific information. Bull. Ent. Soc. America, 14(1): 72-73.

Foote, Richard H. and Gloria M. Hammack. 1969. A system-designed entomological data center, a feasibility study, phase I. Biological Sciences Communication Project, Washington, D. C., ii + 134 pp. + 32 tables.

Lancaster, F. Wilfried. 1968. Information retrieval systems. John Wiley and Sons, N. Y., xiv + 222 pp.

Lipetz, Ben-Ami. 1966. Information storage and retrieval. Scientific American, 215 (September): 224-242.

McCarthy, John *et al.* 1966. Information. Scientific American, 215 (September): 66-260.

Quastler, H. 1967. General principles of systems analysis. *In* Waterman, T. H. and Harold Morowitz (eds.). Theoretical and mathematical biology. Blaisdell Publ. Co., N. Y., pp. 313-333.

SATCOM report, 1969, see Committee on scientific and technical communication, under references to chapter 5.

Chapter 3. Stored Information

Arnett, R. H., Jr. 1969a. Storage and retrieval of information from insect specimens. Ent. News, 80: 197-205.

Arnett, R. H., Jr. 1970. Objectives of a taxonomic catalog of Coleoptera. Coleopt. Bull., 24: 76-84.

Evans, David C. 1966. Computer logic and memory. Scientific American, 215 (September): 74-85.

Chapter 4. Original Documents

Original data books

Evans, Howard E. 1966. The comparative ethology and evolution of the sand wasps. Harvard University Press, Cambridge, xviii + 526 pp.

Krombein, Karl V. 1967. Trap-nesting wasps and bees; life histories, nests, and associates. Smithsonian Institution Press, Washington, D. C., vi + 570 pp., incl. 29 pls.

Roeder, Kenneth D. 1963. Nerve cells and insect behavior. Harvard University Press, Cambridge, xi + 188 pp.

Snodgrass, Robert E. 1951. Comparative studies on the head of mandibulate arthropods. Cornell University Press, Ithaca, viii + 118 pp.

Taxonomic research reports

Bickle, R. L. 1969. A new species of Hydroptilidae (Trichoptera). Ent. News, 80: 79-81.

Evans, Howard E. 1969. Phoretic copulation in Hymenoptera. Ent. News, 80: 113-124.

Timberlake, P. H. 1969. *Metapsaenythia,* a new Pangurine bee genus (Hymenoptera, Andrenidae). Ent. News, 80: 89-92.

Experimental data

Happ, George M., John D. Strandberg, and Christine M. Happ. 1966. The terpene-producing glands of a phasmid insect; cell morphology and histochemistry. Journ. Morph., 119: 143-160.

Moriarty, F. 1969. Water uptake and embryonic development in eggs of *Chorthippus brunneus* Thunberg (Saltatoria: Acrididae). Journ. Exp. Biol., 50: 327-333.

Nagle, J. J. and L. E. Mettler. 1969. Relative fitness of introgressed and parental populations of *Drosophila mojavensis* and *D. arizonensis*. Evolution, 23: 519-524.

Simon, Jean-Pierre. 1969. Comparative serology of a complex species group of food-plant specialists: the *Ragoletis pomonella* complex (Diptera, Tephritidae). Syst. Zool., 18: 169-184.

Yurkiewicz, William J. 1969. Fatty acid composition of limited use in aphid taxonomy. Ent. News, 80: 85-87.

Lists of core journals

Council on Biological Sciences Information. 1970. Selected current primary serial publications in the biological sciences. Fed. American Soc. Exp. Biol., Working Document no. 1, x + 30 pp.

Laffoon, Jean L. 1969. Entomological and archnological serials. Dept. Entomology, Iowa State University, Ames, 33 pp.

Foote, Richard H. and Gloria M. Hammack, 1969. [see p. 170]

Montgomery, B. Elwood. 1967. World list of entomological serials. Department of Entomology, Purdue University, Lafayette, 35 pp.

Lists of peripheral periodicals

Titus, Edna Brown (ed.). 1965. Union list of serials in libraries of the United States and Canada, 3rd ed. H. W. Wilson Co., New York, 5 vols.

Data Documents

Arnett, R. H., Jr. 1970. Data documents, a new publication plan for systematic entomology. Ent. News, 81: 1-11.

Yochelson, Ellis L. 1969. Publication, microfilm, microcard, microfiche, and the International Code of Zoological Nomenclature. Syst. Zool., 18: 476-480.

Series

Freude, Heinz, Karl Wilhelm Harde, and Gustav Adolf Lohse. 1965. Die Käfer Mitteleuropas, band 1: Einführung in die Käferkunde, 214 pp. 1964. Band 4: Staphylinidae I (Micropeplinae bis Tachyporinae), 264 pp. 1967. Band 7: Clavicornia, 310 pp. 1969. Band 8: Teredilia, Heteromera, Lamellicornia, 388 pp. 1966. Band 9: Cerambycidae, Chrysomelidae, 299 pp. Goeche und Evers, Krefeld, Germany.

Hatch, Melville H. 1953. The beetles of the Pacific Northwest, part I: Introduction and Adephaga, vii + 340 pp. 1957. Part II: Staphyliniformia, ix + 384 pp. 1962. Part III: Pselaphidae and Diversicornia I, ix + 502 pp. 1965. Part IV: Macrodactyles, Palpicornes, and Heteromera, viii + 268 pp. *In press:* Part V: Phytophaga, Rhynchophora, and Lamellicornes. University Washington Press, Seattle.

Maps and gazetteers

Grosvenor, Melville B. (ed.) 1963. National Geographic atlas of the world. National Geographic Society, Washington, D. C. 300 pp.

Küchler, A. W. 1964. Map and manual to accompany the map: potential natural vegetation of the conterminous United States. American Geographic Society, special publ. no. 36, v + 38 pp. + 116 pls.

G. and C. Merriam Co. 1960. Webster's geographical dictionary, rev. ed., Springfield, Mass., xxxi + 1293 pp. + 24 maps.

Selander, Richard B. and Patricia Vaurie. 1962. A gazetteer to accompany the "Insecta" volumes of the "Biologia Centrali-Americana". American Mus. Nov., no. 2099, 70 pp.

Times of London. 1967. The times atlas of the world, comprehensive edition. Houghton Mifflin Co., xliii + 272 pp. + 123 maps.

Tapes and disks

Asch, Moses (ed.) 1952. Sounds of a tropical rain forest. Folkways Records and Service Corp., New York, FX 6120.

Saheb-Ettaba, Caroline, and Roger B. McFarland. 1969. ANSCR: The alpha-numeric system for classification of recordings. Bro-Dart Publ. Co., Williamsport, Pa., xvi + 212 pp.

Lanyon, W. E. and W. N. Tavolga. 1960. Animal sounds and communication. Publ. no. 7, American Inst. Biol. Sci., Washington, D.C. xiii + 443 pp. + 1 disk.

Chapter 5. Preparation of Documents for Information Storage

Brown, Roland W. 1954. Composition of scientific words. Washington, D. C. 882 pp.

Committee on scientific and technical communication. 1969. Scientific and technical communication (SATCOM report). National Academy of Science, Washington, D. C. (publ. 1707), xiii + 322 pp.

Conference of biological editors, committee on form and style. 1964. Style manual for biological journals, 2nd ed. American Inst. Biol. Sci., Washington, D. C. x + 117 pp.

International Paper. 1966. Pocket pal, a graphic arts digest for printers and advertising production managers, New York, 190 pp.

Miles, S. R. 1957. How to make tables of information. Purdue University Agricultural Experiment Station, 86 pp.

Woodford, F. Peter. 1968. Scientific writing for graduate students. Rockefeller University Press, New York, x + 190 pp.

Chapter 6. Preparation of Documents for Information Retrieval

(For a full discussion of the International Code of Zoological Nomenclature, see Blackwelder, 1967, under "methods", below.)

Barber, H. S. and J. C. Bridwell. 1940. Dejean Catalogue names (Coleoptera). Bull. Brooklyn Ent. Soc., 35: 1-12.

Blackwelder, Richard E. 1949. Studies on the dates of books on Coleoptera, I, II, III. Coleopt. Bull., 3: 42-46; 76; 92-94.

Blackwelder, Richard E. 1949. An adventure in bibliochronology. Journ. Washington Acad. Sci., 39: 301-305.

Blackwelder, Richard E. 1952. The generic names of the beetle family Staphylinidae with an essay on genotypy. Bull. United States Nat. Mus., 200. 483 pp.

Custer, Benjamin A. (ed.). 1965. Dewey descimal classification and relative index devised by Melvil Dewey, 9th abridged ed. Forest Press, Inc., Lake Placid, N. Y. vi + 594 pp.

Gilmour, J. S. L. *et al.* (eds.). 1969. International code of nomenclature of cultivated plants—1969. International Bureau for Plant Taxonomy and Nomenclature of the International Association for Plant Taxonomy. Utrecht, Netherlands, 32 pp.

Gould, Sydney W. 1954. Permanent numbers to supplement the binominal system of nomenclature. American Scientist, 42: 269-274.

Lanjouw, J. *et al.* (eds.) 1966. International code of botanical nomenclature. International Bureau for Plant Taxonomy and Nomenclature of the International Association for Plant Taxonomy, Utrecht, Netherlands, 402 pp.

Sabrosky, C. W. 1967. Zoological nomenclature in the jet age. Proc. Helminth. Soc. Washington, 34: 236-240.

Savory, Theodore. 1962. Naming the living world. John Wiley and Sons, Inc., New York, xiii + 128 pp.

Stoll, N. R. (ed.). 1961. Code international de nomenclature zoologique adopté par le XV^c Congrès international de zoologie. International Trust on Zoological Nomenclature, London, xviii + 176 pp.

Stoll, N. R. (ed.). 1964. International code of zoological nomenclature, 2nd ed. International Trust for Zoological Nomenclature, London, 174 pp.

Thomas A. Crowell Co. 1962. Roget's international thesaurus, 3rd ed., New York, xx + 1250 pp.

Chapter 7. Search resources

Chamberlin, W. J. 1952. Entomological nomenclature and literature, 3rd ed. Wm. C. Brown Co., Dubuque, Iowa, vii + 141.

Derksen, Walter and Ursula Scheiding. 1963. Index litteraturae entomologicae, (1864-1900). Ser. 2, vol. 1, A-E, xii + 697 pp.; 1965, vol. 2, F-L, 679 pp., Berlin.

Farrier, Maurice H. 1969. Some information-retrieval tools little known to entomologists. Bull. Ent. Soc. America, 15: 371-372.

Horn, Walther and S. Schenkling. 1928-1929. Index litteraturae entomologicae. Berlin, 1426 pp.

Katz, William A. 1969. Introduction to reference works; vol. 1, basic information sources. McGraw-Hill Book Co., New York, xi + 376 pp.; 1969. Vol. 2, Reference service, xi + 254 pp.

Kerker, Ann E. and Henry T. Murphy. 1968. Biological and biomedical resource literature. Purdue University, Lafayette, ix + 226 pp.

Smith, R. C. 1967. Guide to the literature of the zoological sciences, 7th ed. Burgess Publ. Co., St. Paul, xii + 232 pp.

Chapter 8. Abstracts and indexes

Biological Abstracts. 1969. Guide to the indexes for Biological Abstracts and Bioresearch Index. Biosciences Information Service, Philadelphia, 20 pp.

Biological Abstracts. 1970. Guide to the preparation of abstracts. Biological Abstracts, 51 (1): Jan. 1 issue. [Revised and/or republished each year.]

Bridges, Kent W. 1970. Automatic indexing of personal bibliographies. Bioscience, 20 (2): 94-97.

Broadhurst, P. L. 1962. Coordinate indexing: a bibliographic aid. American Psychol., 17 (3): 137-142.

Documentation, Inc. 1955. The uniterm system of indexing: operation manual. Washington, D. C. 47 pp.

National Federation of Science Abstracting and Indexing Services. 1963. Guide to the world's abstracting and indexing services in science and technology. Washington, D. C. 183 pp.

Schallau, Con and Carl A. Newport. 1969. Uniterm coordinate indexing—a system for maintaining reference collections. Journ. Forest. 67: 246-247.

Chapter 9. Synthesized information

Reviews

Arnett, R. H., Jr. 1953. A review of the beetle family Cephaloidae. Proc. United States Nat. Mus., 103 (no. 3321): 155-161.

Pate, V. S. L. 1947. Neotropical Sapygidae with a conspectus of the family (Hymenoptera: Aculeata). Acta Zool. Lilloana Inst. Miguel Lillo, 4: 393-426.

Revisions

Braun, Ralph A. 1967. Contributions to the mosquito fauna of Southeast Asia, II: the genus *Culex* in Thailand (Diptera: Culicidae). Contr. American Ent. Inst., 2 (1), iii + 296 pp.

Cohn, Theodore J. 1965. The arid-land katydids of the North American genus *Neobarrettia* (Orthoptera: Tettigoniidae); their systematics and a reconstruction of their history. Misc. Publ. Mus. Zool. Univ. Michigan, no. 126, 179 pp.

Freytag, Paul H. and William P. Morrison. 1969. A preliminary study of the Idiocerinae of Chile (Homoptera: Cicadellidae). Ent. News, 80: 285-292.

Kistner, David H. 1969. Revision of the termitophilous subfamily Trichopseniinae (Coleoptera, Staphylinidae); I. The genus *Schizelythron* Kemner. Ent. News, 80: 44-53.

Rentz, David C. and James D. Birchim. 1968. Revisionary studies in the Nearctic Decticinae. Mem. Pacific Coast Ent. Soc., vol. 3, (xvi) + 173 pp.

Ryckman, Raymond E. 1962. Biosystematics and hosts of the *Triatoma protracta* complex in North America (Hemiptera: Reduviidae) (Rodentia: Cricetidae). Univ. California Publ. Ent., 27(2): 93-240, 24 pls.

Vaurie, Patricia. 1968. Review of South American genus *Belopoeus* Schoenheer (Coleoptera, Curculionidae, Rhynchophorinae). Coleopt. Bull., 22: 39-44.

Willis, Harold L. 1967. Bionomics and zoogeography of tiger beetles of saline habitats in the central United States (Coleoptera: Cicindelidae). Univ. Kansas Sci. Bull., 47(5): 145-313.

Monographs

Busnel, R.–G. (ed.). 1963. Acoustic behaviour of animals. Elsevier Publ. Co., N. Y., xx + 933 pp.

von Frisch, Karl (translated by Leigh E. Chadwick). 1967. The dance language and orientation of bees. Harvard University Press, Cambridge, xiv + 566 pp.

Gregg, Robert C. 1963. The ants of Colorado. Univ. Colorado Press, Boulder, xvi + 792 pp.

Korschelt, E. 1923-1924. Der gelbrand *Dytiscus marginalis* L. W. Engelmann, Leipzig, 2 vols.

Usinger, Robert L. 1966. Monograph of Cimicidae (Hemiptera, Heteroptera). Thomas Say Foundation, vol. 7, xi + 585 pp.

Introductory textbooks

Borrer, Donald J. and Dwight M. Delong. 1970. An introduction to the study of insects, 3rd ed. Holt, Rinehart, and Winston, New York.

Comstock, John Henry. 1940. An introduction to entomology, 9th ed. Cornell University Press, Ithaca, xix + 1064 pp.

Essig, E. O. 1942. College entomology. Macmillan Co., New York, vii + 900 pp.

Graham, Samuel A. and Fred B. Knight. 1965. Principles of forest entomology, 4th ed. McGraw-Hill Book Co., New York, xii + 417 pp.

Little, V. A. 1963. General and applied entomology, 2nd ed. Harper and Row, New York, x + 543 pp.

Matheson, Robert. 1950. Entomology for introductory courses, 2nd ed. Cornell University Press, Ithaca, xiv + 629 pp.

Matheson, Robert. 1951. Laboratory guide in entomology for introductory courses, 2nd ed., Cornell University Press, vii + 135 pp.

Richards, D. W. and R. G. Davies. 1964. A general textbook of entomology (originally by A. D. Imms), 9th ed. rev. Methuen and Co., London, ix + 886 pp.

Ross, Herbert H. 1965. A textbook of entomology, 3rd ed. John Wiley and Sons, New York, xi + 539 pp.

Insect anatomy

Balfour-Browne, F. 1932. A textbook of practical entomology. Longmans, Greene, and Co., New York, viii + 191 pp.

Bradley, J. Chester. 1939. A laboratory guide to the study of the evolution of the wings of insects, 2nd ed. Daw, Illston and Co., Ithaca, 60 pp. + 83 pls.

Comstock, John Henry. 1918. The wings of insects. Cornell University Press, Ithaca, 430 pp.

DuPorte, E. Melville. 1959. Manual of insect morphology. Reinhold Publ. Co., New York, xi + 224 pp.

Johannsen, O. A. and F. H. Butt. 1941. Embryology of insects and myriopods. McGraw-Hill Book Co., New York, xi + 462 pp.

Matsuda, Ryuichi. 1965. Morphology and evolution of the insect head. Mem. American Ent. Inst., no. 4 [vii] + 334 pp.

Snodgrass, Robert E. 1935. Principles of insect morphology. McGraw-Hill Book Co., New York, ix + 668 pp.

Insect physiology

Patton, Robert L. 1963. Introductory insect physiology. W. B. Saunders Co., Philadelphia, vi + 245 pp.

Rockstein, Morris. 1964. The physiology of insecta, vol. 1, xiv + 640 pp.; 1965. vol. 2, xvi + 905 pp.; 1964, vol. 3, xiv + 692 pp. Academic Press, New York.

Wigglesworth, Vincent B. 1965. The principles of insect physiology, 6th ed. Methuen and Co., London, viii + 741 pp.

Insect ecology

Chapman, Royal N. 1931. Animal ecology, with especial reference to insects. McGraw-Hill Book Co., New York, x + 464 pp.

Clausen, C. P. 1962 (reprint). Entomolophagous insects. Hafner Publ. Co., New York, x + 688 pp.

Insect taxonomy

(For an extensive listing of useful works on insect taxonomy, see Borrer and Delong, 1970, under general textbooks, above.)

Brues, C. T., A. L. Melander, and Frank M. Carpenter. 1954. Classification of insects. Bull. Museum of Comp. Zool., vol. 108, vi + 917 pp.

Methods

Arnett, R. H., Jr. 1967a. Locality and data labels for insects. Ann. Ent. Soc. America, 60: 1111-1112.

Bailey, N. T. 1959. Statistical methods in biology. John Wiley and Sons, New York, ix + 200 pp.

Blackwelder, Richard E. 1967. Taxonomy, a text and reference book. John Wiley and Sons, New York, xiv + 698 pp.

Ferris, Gordon F. 1928. The principles of systematic entomology. Stanford University Press, Palo Alto, 169 pp.

Holmann, H. H. 1962. Biological research methods. Hafner Publ. Co., viii + 262 pp.

Mayr, Ernst. 1969. Principles of systematic zoology. McGraw-Hill Book Co., New York, xi + 428 pp.

Needham, James G. (ed.). 1959 (reprint). Culture methods for invertebrate animals. Dover Publ. Co., New York, xxxii + 590 pp.

Papp, Charles S. 1968. Scientific illustration: theory and practice. Wm. C. Brown Co., Dubuque, 340 pp.

Peterson, Alvah. 1955. A manual of entomological technique, 8th ed. Edwards Bros., Ann Arbor, v + 367 pp.

Simpson, G. G., Anne Roe, and R. C. Lewontin. 1960. Quantitative zoology, rev. ed. Harcourt, Brace, and Co., New York, vii + 440 pp.

Smith, Carroll N., 1966. Insect colonization and mass production. Academic Press, New York, xxi + 618 pp.

Sokal, Robert R. and Peter H. A. Sneath. 1963. Principles of numerical taxonomy. W. H. Freeman and Co., xvi + 359 pp.

Southwood, T. R. E. 1966. Ecological methods with particular reference to the study of insect populations. Methuen and Co., London, xviii + 391 pp.

Zweifel, Frances W. 1961. A handbook of biological illustrations. University of Chicago Press, Chicago, xv + 131 pp.

Pest management

DeBach, Paul (ed.). 1964. Biological control of insect pests and weeds. Reinhold Publ. Co., New York, xxiv + 844 pp.

Horsfall, William R. 1962. Medical entomology. Ronald Press Co., New York, ix + 467 pp.

James, Maurice T. and Robert F. Harwood. 1969. Hermes's Medical entomology, 6th ed. Macmillan Co., New York, ix + 484 pp.

Mallis, Arnold. 1969. Handbook of pest control. McNair-Dorland Co., New York, 1158 pp.

Matheson, Robert. 1950. Medical entomology, 2nd ed. Cornell University Press, Ithaca, xi + 612 pp.

Metcalf, C. L., W. P. Flint, and R. L. Metcalf. 1962. Destructive and useful insects, 4th ed. McGraw-Hill Book Co., New York, xii + 1087 pp.

Pfad, Robert E. (ed.). 1962. Fundamentals of applied entomology. Macmillan Co., New York, x + 668 pp.

Steinhaus, Edward A. 1967 (reprint). Insect microbiology. Hafner Publ. Co., New York, xi + 763 pp.

Steinhaus, Edward A. 1967 (reprint). Principles of insect pathology. Hafner Publ. Co., New York, xi + 757 pp.

Subcommittee on Insect Pests. 1969. Insect-pest management and control. *In* Principles of plant and animal pest control. Vol. 3. National Academy of Science, publ. no. 1695, xxii + 508 pp.

Sweetman, Harvey I. 1958. The principles of biological control. Wm. C. Brown Co., Dubuque, xii + 560 pp.

Current status publications

Dobzhansky, T., M. K. Hecht and W. C. Steere (eds.). 1967+. Evolutionary biology. Vol. 1+. Appleton, Century, Crofts, New York.

Johnston, R. F. (ed.). 1970+. Annual review of ecology and systematics. Vol. 1+. Annual Reviews, Inc., Palo Alto.

Smith, R. F. and T. E. Mittler (eds.). 1956+. Annual review of entomology. Vol. 1+. Annual Reviews, Inc., Palo Alto.

Glossaries

Henderson, I. F., W. D. Henderson, and J. H. Kenneth. 1960. A dictionary of biological terms, 8th ed. Van Nostrand, Rinehold and Co., Inc., New York, xvi + 640 pp.

Ericson, Ruth D. 1961. A glossary of some foreign language terms in entomology. United States Dept. Agric. Handbook no. 218, 59 pp.

Lindroth, Carl H. 1957. The principle terms used for male and female genitalia in Coleoptera. Opuscula Ent., 22: 241-256.

Torre-Bueno, J. R. de la. 1937. A glossary of entomology. Brooklyn Ent. Soc., ix + 336 pp. 3 8 pls.

Tulloch, George S. 1960. Torre-Bueno's glossary of entomology—Supplement A. Brooklyn Ent. Soc., 36 pp.

Tuxen, S. L. (ed.). 1970. Taxonomist's glossary of genitalia in insects, 2nd ed. Munksgaard, Copenhagen, 359 pp.

History

Cushing, Emory C. 1957. History of entomology in World War II. Smithsonian Institution, Washington, D. C. (publ. no. 4294), vi + 117 pp.

Essig, E. O. 1965 (reprint). A history of entomology. Hafner Publ. Co., vii + 1029 pp.

Weiss, Harry B. and Grace M. Ziegler. 1931. Thomas Say, early American naturalist. Charles C. Thomas, Springfield, Ill., xiv + 260 pp.

Expeditions

Ball, George E. and Donald R. Whitehead. 1967. Localities for collectin Mexico. Coleopt. Bull., 21: 122-138.

Bradley, J. Chester. 1919. An entomological cross-section of the United States. Scientific Monthly, April, May, June issues. (Reprint, 54 pp.)

Evans, Howard E. 1952. (Report of research expedition in Mexico). Year Book of the American Philosophical Society for 1951, pp. 139-141.

Howden, H. F. 1966. Entomological ramblings in Mexico. Coleopt. Bull., 20: 19-26, 3 maps.

Michelbacher, A. E. and E. S. Ross. 1942. Contributions toward a knowledge of the insect fauna of Lower California. Proc. California Acad. Sci. (4th ser.), 24 (1): 1-20, 3 pls.

Munroe, Eugene. 1963. Collecting insects in the territory of Papua and New Guinea, 1957. Proc. Ninth Pacific Sci. Cong., 1957, 9: 32-41.

Peterson, Børge. 1966. The Noona Dan expedition, 1961-1962; insects and other land arthropods. Ent. Meddel., 34: 283-304.

Triplehorn, Charles A. 1966. Entomologia no Brasil vista por um entomologista Norte-Americano. O Biologico, 32: 5-12.

Vaurie, Charles and Patricia. 1949. Insect collecting in Guatemala 65 years after Champion. Journ. New York Ent. Soc., 57: 1-18.

Vaurie, Patricia and Charles. 1954. Collecting in Sonora, Mexico, including Tiburon Island. Journ. New York Ent. Soc., 61: 79-91.

Catalogs

Blickenstaff, C. C. (ed.). 1965. Common names of insects. Bull Ent. Soc. America, 11 (4): 287-320.

Claasen, Peter W. 1940. A catalogue of the Plecoptera of the World. Cornell University Agric. Exp. Sta., Mem. 232, 235 pp.

Drake, Carl J. and Florence A. Ruhoff. 1965. Lacebugs of the World: a catalog (Hemiptera: Tingidae). United States Nat. Mus. Bull., 243, viii + 634 pp.

Junk, W. (puslisher) and S. Schenkling (editor). 1910-1940. Coleopterorum Catalogus, 170 parts, 31 vols., Dr. W. Junk, N. V., The Hague, Netherlands.

Junk, W. (publisher) and W. O. Steel (editor). 1950+. Coleopterorum Catalogus Supplementa. 17+ parts. Dr. W. Junk, N. V., The Hague, Netherlands.

Leonard, Mortimer D. (ed.). 1928. A list of the insects of New York with a list of the spiders and certain other allied groups. Cornell University Agric. Exp. Sta., Mem. 101, 1121 pp.

McDunnough, J. 1938. Checklist of the Lepidoptera of Canada and the United States of America, pt. 1, Mem. Southern California Acad. Sci., vol. 1, 272 pp.; 1939, Part 2, vol. 2, 171 pp.

Muesebeck, C. F. W., K. V. Krombein, and Henry K. Townes. 1951. Hymenoptera of America north of Mexico, synoptic catalog. United States Dept. Agric. Monograph no. 2, 1420 pp. + 1 map. 1958. First supplement, 305 pp. + separate host index, 3 pp. 1967. Second supplement, 584 pp.

Sabrosky, Curtis W. 1967. Corrections to a catalog of the Diptera of America north of Mexico. Bull. Ent. Soc. America, 13: 115-125.

Snyder, Thomas E. 1949. Catalog of the termites (Isoptera) of the World. Smithsonian Misc. Coll., vol. 112 (publ. 3953), 490 pp.

Stone, Alan, *et al.* (eds.). 1965. A catalog of the Diptera of America north of Mexico. United States Dept. Agric. Handbook no. 276, 1696 pp.

Nomenclators

Agassiz, Louis. 1846. Nomenclatoris zoologici. Index universalis. Soloduri, 393 pp.

de Marschall, August. 1873. Nomenclator zoologicus. Vendobonae, 482 pp.

Neave, S. A. 1939-1950. Nomenclator zoologicus. Zool. Soc. London, 4 vols., 1 suppl.

Schulze, F. E., W. Kukenthal, and K. Heiden. 1926-1940. Nomenclator animalium generum et subgenerum. Preuss. Akad. Wissensch., Berlin.

Scudder, S. H. 1882. Nomenclator zoologicus (1758-1879). Bull. United States Nat. Mus., no. 19.

Sherborn, C. D. 1902. Index animalium (1758-1800). Sect. 1. Cambridge University Press, Cambridge, 1195 pp.

Sherborn, C. D. 1922-1933. Index animalium (1800-1850). Sect. 2, 33 volumes. Cambridge University Press, Cambridge.

Waterhouse, C. O. 1902. Index zoologicus (1864-1900). Zool. Soc. London.

Waterhouse, C. O. 1912. Index zoologicus (1901-1910). No. 2. Zool. Soc. London.

Dictionaries

Grove, Philip B. (ed.). 1961. Webster's third new international dictionary. G. and C. Merriam Co., Springfield, Mass. 2662 pp.

Stein, Jess (ed.). 1966. The Random House dictionary of the English language. Random House, New York, 2059 pp.

de Vries, L. 1959. German-English Science Dictionary, 3rd ed. McGraw-Hill Book Co., New York.

de Vries, L. 1962. French-English Science Dictionary, 3rd ed. McGraw-Hill Book Co., New York.

Encyclopedias

Altman, P. L. and D. S. Dittner (eds.). 1964. Biology data book. Federation of American Soc. Exper. Biol., xix + 633 pp.

Long, Luman H. (ed.). 1968. The world almanac and book of facts, 100 ed. Doubleday and Co., New York, 912 pp.

Kurtz, Seymour. 1969. Encyclopedia almanac, 1970. The New York Times, New York, 1056 pp.

Schroder, C. W. M. 1925-1929. Handbuch der entomologie. G. Fischer, Jena, 3 vols.

Lameere, A. 1932-1942. Précis de zoologie, 2nd ed., vols. 4 and 5, Paris.

Handlirsch, A. 1926-1936. Insects. *In* Kukenthal, W. and T. Krombach (eds.). Handbuch de zoologie, v. 4, pp. 403-2756.

Grassé, Pierre–P. (ed.). 1951. Traité de Zoologie. Vol. 10, 2 fascicles, 1948 pp. Paris.

Handbooks, Manuals, Regional Works

Arnett, R. H., Jr. 1968. The beetles of the United States, 2nd printing. slightly rev. American Ent. Inst., Ann Arbor, 1112 pp.

Needham, James G. and Minter J. Westfall, Jr. 1955. A manual of the dragonflies of North America (Anisoptera) including the Greater Antilles and the provinces of the Mexican border. University of California Press, Berkeley, xii + 615 pp.

Smart, John. 1965. A handbook for the identification of insects of medical importance, 4th ed. British Museum (Natural History), London, xi + 303 pp., + 13 pls.

Stannard, Lewis J. 1968. The thrips, or Thysanoptera of Illinois. Bull. Illinois Nat. Hist. Surv., 29(4) [vi+]: 215-552.

Chapter 10. Popular literature

Pamphlets

Lehker, Glenn E. and Howard O. Day. 1969. How to collect, preserve, and identify insects. Cooperative Ext. Serv., Purdue University, Lafayette, Ext. Circular 509, 43 pp.

Mumford, Bessie C. (compiler). 1966. List of intercepted plant pests, 1965. United States Dept. of Agric., 88 pp.

Trade publications

Borrer, Donald J. and Richard E. White. 1970. A field guide to the insects of America north of Mexico. Houghton Mifflin Co., Boston, 416 pp.

Carson, Rachel. 1962. Silent spring. Houghton Mifflin Co., Boston, xiii + 368 pp.

Cheesman, Evelyn. 1953. Insects, their secret world. William Sloane Associates, New York, vii + 246 pp.

Chu, H. F. 1949. How to know the immature insects. Wm. C. Brown Co., Dubuque, Iowa, vi + 234 pp.

Jaques, H. E. 1947. How to know the insects, 2nd ed. Wm. C. Brown Co., Dubuque, Iowa, iv + 205 pp.

Jaques, H. E. 1951. How to know the beetles. Wm. C. Brown Co., Dubuque, Iowa, 372 pp.

Klots, Alexander B. 1951. A field guide to the butterflies. Houghton Mifflin Co., Boston, xvi + 349 pp.

Frost, S. W. 1959 (reprint). Insect life and insect natural history, 2nd ed., rev. Dover Publ. Co., New York, viii + 526 pp.

Lutz, Frank E. 1948. Field book of insects, rev. ed. G. P. Putnam's Sons, New York, 510 pp.

Swain, Ralph B. 1952. The insect guide. Doubleday and Co., Garden City, xlvi + 261 pp.

Wigglesworth, Vincent B. 1964. The life of insects. Weidenfeld and Nicolson, London, xii + 360 pp.

Zim, Herbert S. and Clarence Cottam. 1951. Insects, a guide to familar American insects. Simon and Schuster (A golden nature guide), New York, 160 pp.

Chapter 11. Societies, Institutions, and Personnel

Directories

American Institute of Biological Sciences. 1967. Directory of bioscience departments in the United States and Canada. Rinehold Publ. Co., New York, xvi + 672 pp.

Arnett, R. H., Jr. and G. Allan Samuelson. 1969. Directory of Coleoptera collections of North America (Canada through Panama). Purdue University, Lafayette, vii + 123 pp.

Blackwelder, Richard E. and Ruth M. 1961. Directory of zoological taxonomists of the World. Southern Illinois University Press, Carbondale, xvii + 404 pp.

Horn, Walther and Ilse Kahle. 1935-1937. Uber entomologische sammlungen, entomologen und entomo-museologie. Entomologische Beihefte, vol. 2-4, pts. 1-3, vi + 536 pp., 38 pls.; 1935, suppl., vol. 2, 12 pp.

Joint Committee on Printing. 1969. Official congressional directory. United States Government Printing Office, Washington, D. C.

Murdoch, Wallace P. (ed.). 1969. Entomological Society of America membership list. Bull. Ent. Soc. America, 15(4): 261-342.

Sachtleben, Hans. 1961. Nachtrage zu "Walter Horn and Ilse Kable: Uber entomologische sammlungen." Beitr. Ent., 11: 481-550.

United States Department of Agriculture. 1965. Directory of organization and field activities of the Department of Agriculture. Agric. Handbook no. 76.

Walker, R. L. (ed.). 1969. Colonies of insects, mites, ticks, spiders, and insect cell lines maintained in laboratories of the entomology research and market quality research division of the Agriculture Research Service, United States Department of Agriculture, rev. ed. Pesticide Chemical Research Branch, United States Dept. Agric., Beltsville, 89 pp.

Institutional publications

British Museum publications, see Bernard Quaritch, Ltd., 1969. A catalog of publications distributed by Bernard Quaritch. [See list of dealers in Appendix II.]

United States Government Printing Office. Bimonthly list of publications and motion pictures. United States Dept. Agric., Washington, D. C.

Field stations

Vernberg, F. John. 1963. Field stations in the United States. American Zool., 3 (3): 245-386.

Preserved areas

Committee on the study of plant and animal communities. 1951. Nature sanctuaries in the United States and Canada. The Living

Wilderness, 15 (35): 1-46.

Edwards, Ernest P. 1968. Finding birds in Mexico, 2nd ed. Sweet Brier, Virginia, xxvii + 282 pp. + 14 pls.

Federal Committee on Research Natural Areas. 1968. A directory of research natural areas on federal lands of the United States of America. United States Government Printing Office, Washington, 129 pp.

Lindsey, Alton A., Damian V. Schmelz, and Stanley A. Nichols. 1969. Natural areas in Indiana and their preservation. Purdue University, Lafayette, xi + 594 pp.

National Geographic Book Service. 1959. America's Wonderlands, the scenic national parks and monuments of the United States. National Geographic Society, Washington, D. C. 512 pp.

Nicholson, E. M. 1968. Handbook to the conservation section of the International Biological Programme. Blackwell Scientific Publ., Oxford, x + 84 pp.

Peterken, G. F. 1967. Guide to the checksheet for IBP areas. Blackwell Scientific Publ., Oxford, x + 133 pp. + 11 checksheets.

Shelford, Victor E. 1926. Naturalist's guide to the Americas. William and Wilkins, Baltimore, xv + 761 pp.

Current project lists

PCL Publications. 1969. The naturalist's directory (International), 40th ed. PCL Publications, Spring Lake, N. J.

Bibliographies

Besterman, T. 1950. A world bibliography of bibliographies, 2nd ed. London, 3 vols.

Carpenter, Mathilde M. 1945. Bibliography of biographies of entomologists. American Midl. Nat., 33: 1-116 pp.; 1953. Supplement, 50: 257-348.

Jacques Cattell Press (eds.). 1965-1968. American men of science, 11th ed. R. R. Bowker Co., New York, 6 vols.

APPENDIX II

A SELECTED LIST OF COMMERCIAL PUBLISHERS AND DEALERS IN ENTOMOLOGICAL LITERATURE

Academic Press, Inc., 111 5th Ave., New York, NY 10003
American Elsevier Publishing Co., Inc., 52 Vanderbilt Ave., New York, NY 10017
American Entomological Institute, 5950 Warren Road, Ann Arbor, MI 48105
Antiquariaat Junk, Postbus 5, Lochem, Holland
A. Asher and Co., 386 Herengracht, Amsterdam-C, Holland
Barnes and Noble, Inc., 105 Fifth Ave., New York, NY 10003
Bio-Rand Foundation, Inc., 1330 Dillon Heights Ave., Baltimore, MD 21228
E. J. Brill, Oude Rijn, 33a-35, Leiden, Holland
Wm. C. Brown Co., see Kendall/Hunt
Burgess Publishing Co., 426 S. Sixth St., Minneapolis, MN 55415
Cambridge University Press, 32 E. 57th St., New York, NY 10022
E. W. Classey, 353 Hanworth Road, Hampton, Middlesex, England
Cornell University Press, 124 Roberts Place, Ithaca, NY 14851

Cranbrook Institute of Science, Bloomfield Hills, MI 48013

Doubleday and Co., Inc., 501 Franklin Ave., Garden City, NY 11531

Dover Publications, Inc., 180 Varick St., New York, NY 10014

E. P. Dutton and Co., Inc., 201 Park Ave. S., New York, NY 10003

J. W. Edwards, Publishers, Inc., 2500 S. State St., Ann Arbor, MI 48104

Entomological Reprint Specialists, P.O. Box 207, East Lansing, MI 48823

Field Museum of Natural History, Roosevelt Road and Lake Shore Drive, Chicago, IL 60605

Golden Press, Inc., 850 Third Ave., New York, NY 10022

Hafner Publishing Co., Inc., 31 E. 10th St., New York, NY 10003

Harper and Row, Publishers, Inc., 49 E. 33rd St., New York, NY 10016

Harvard University Press, 79 Garden St., Cambridge, MA 02138

Holden-Day, Inc., 500 Sansome St., San Francisco, CA 94111

Holt, Rinehart and Winston, Inc., 383 Madison Ave., New York, NY 10017

Houghton Mifflin Co., 2 Park St., Boston, MA 02107

Kendall/Hunt Publishing Co., 131 South Locust St., Dubuque, IA 52001 [Successor to Wm. C. Brown Book Company.]

Longmans, Green and Co., Inc., see David McKay Co., Inc.

Eric Lundberg, Aston, MD 20701

The Macmillan Co., 60 Fifth Ave., New York, NY 10011

McGraw-Hill Book Co., Inc., 330 W. 42nd St., New York, NY 10036

David McKay Co., Inc., 750 Third Ave., New York, NY 10017

Methuen and Co., Ltd., 11, New Felter Lane, London, EC 4, England

Museum of Comparative Zoology, Cambridge, MA 02138

Natural History Books, John Johnson, R.F.D. 2, North Bennington, VT 05257

Natural History Press, see Doubleday and Co., Inc.

Prentice-Hall, Inc., Englewood Cliffs, NJ 07631

G. P. Putnam's Sons, 200 Madison Ave., New York, NY 10016

Quadrangle Books, Inc., 180 N. Wacker Dr., Chicago, IL 60606

Bernard Quaritch, Ltd., 5-8 Lower John St., Golden Square, London, W1V6AB, England

Reinhold Publishing Co., see Van Nostrand, Reinhold Co., Inc.

The Ronald Press Co., 15 E. 26th St., New York, NY 10010

W. B. Saunders Co., W. Washington Square, Philadelphia, PA 19105

Smithsonian Press, Washington, DC 20560

Stanford University Press, Stanford, CA 94305 [Sales only to book-stores.]

Stechert-Hafner, Inc., 31 East 10th St., New York, NY 10003

The Superintendent of Documents, United States Government Printing Office, Washington, DC 20402

Charles C. Thomas, Publisher, 301-327 E. Lawrence Ave., Springfield, IL 62703

Henry Trip, 92-06 Jamaica Ave., Woodhaven, NY 11421

University of California Press, 2223 Fulton St., Berkeley, CA 94720

University of Chicago Press, 5750 Ellis Ave., Chicago, IL 60637

University of Colorado Press, Regent Hall, Box 22, Boulder, CO 80302

University of Florida Press, 15 N.W. 15th St., Gainesville, FL 32603

University of Illinois Press, Urbana, IL 61803

University of Minnesota Press, 2037 University Ave., S.E., Minneapolis, MN 55455

University of North Dakota Press, Grand Forks, ND 58201

University of Texas Press, Austin, TX 78712

University of Toronto Press, Toronto, Ontario, Canada

University of Washington Press, Seattle, WA 98105

Van Nostrand, Reinhold Co., Inc., 120 Alexander St., Princeton, NJ 08540

Weldon and Wesley, Lytton Lodge, Codicote, Hitchin, Herts., England

John Wiley and Sons, Inc., 605 Third Ave., New York, NY 10016

APPENDIX III

ENTOMOLOGICAL EQUIPMENT AND
SUPPLY COMPANIES

Arthropod Specialities Co., P.O. Box 1973, Sacramento, CA 95809 [Suppliers of micro-vials.]

Bio-Equip, Inc., Box 61, Santa Monica, CA 90406 [for west of the Mississippi orders.]
1111 Rolling Road, Baltimore, MD 21228 [for east of the Mississippi orders.]
[Great variety of entomological equipment and supplies.]

Carolina Biological Supply Co., Burlington, NC 27215

Combined Scientific Supplies, P.O. Box 125, Rosemead, CA 91770 [for insect specimens in particular.]

Entomology Research Institute, Lake City, MN 55041

General Biological Supply House, Inc., 8200 South Hoyne Ave., Chicago, IL 60620

Lane Science Equipment Co., 105 Chambers St., New York, NY 10007

Poly-Ento. Co., Box 3239, San Francisco, CA 94019 [for polyethylene tray bottoms.]

The Steel Fixture Manufacturing Co., P.O. Box 917, Topeka, KS 66601 [for insect drawer cabinets.]

Ward's Natural Science Establishment, Inc., P.O. Box 1712, Rochester, NY 14603

APPENDIX IV

MAJOR ENTOMOLOGICAL LIBRARIES
OF THE UNITED STATES AND CANADA

Academy of Natural Sciences Library, Philadelphia
American Museum of Natural History Library, New York
California Academy of Sciences Library, San Francisco
Canadian National Collection Library, Ottawa
Comstock Memorial Library, Cornell University, Ithaca
Library of Congress, Washington, D.C.
Field Museum of Natural History Library, Chicago
University of Florida Library, Gainesville
University of Illinois Library, Urbana
University of Kansas Library, Lawrence
University of Michigan Library, Ann Arbor
Museum of Comparative Zoology Library, Cambridge
National Agricultural Library, Beltsville
University of North Carolina Library, Raleigh
Ohio State University Library, Columbus

Smithsonian Institution Library, Washington, D.C.
Yale University Library, New Haven

AUTHOR INDEX

Agassiz, Louis, 184
Alexander, Richard, 56
Altman, P. L., 184
Arnett, R. H., Jr., 3, 30, 39, 56,
    63, 99, 170, 171, 172, 176,
    179, 185, 186.
Asch, Moses, 173

Bailey, N. T., 179
Balfour-Browne, F., 178
Ball, George E., 182
Barber, H. S., 102, 174
Bean, James L., 170
Becker, Joseph, 170
Besterman, T., 188
Bickle, R. L., 171
Biological Abstracts, 176
Birchim, James D., 177
Blackwelder, Richard E., 102,

138, 174, 180, 187
Blackwelder, Ruth M., 187
Blickenstaff, C. C., 183
Borrer, Donald J., 178, 179,
    185
Bourne, Charles P., 170
Bradley, J. Chester, 178, 182
Braun, Ralph A., 177
Bridges, Kent W., 126, 176
Bridwell, J. C., 102, 174
British Museum, 187
Broadhurst, P. L., 176
Brown, Roland W., 174
Brown, W. S., 170
Brues, C. T., 179
Busnel, R.–G., 177
Butt, F. H., 179

Carpenter, Frank M., 179

196

SUBJECT INDEX

Words in the glossary are not indexed, nor are any of the names of societies, libraries, publishers, and business firms listed in the appendixes.

POSTFACE

The writing of this text was finished during the waning hours of 1969, the close of a decade. I cannot help but wonder what changes will come during this new decade of the '70's, for change is in the wind and change will come even to entomological literature. I suspect we are nearing the end of the formal, bulky journals as we know them and certainly we may look forward to the development of extremely useful data banks with widely available institutional hook-ups. The individual as the generator of information will almost entirely disappear to be replaced by teams programmed for organizing, researching, processing, and reprocessing data. I hope I have been bold enough in these pages to have this book serve our needs in entomology for a short while, but if it accomplishes its purpose, very soon it will be out of date.

—Ross H. Arnett, Jr.

COLOPHON

The text of this edition was set in Times Roman, a typeface designed by Stanley Morison for *The Times* of London and first used by that newspaper. It is now a very popular face for both text and magazine because it is compact and easy to read. The san-serf is Univers. The book is printed on white Interstate English finish paper and bound in Bancroft Arrestox cloth.